PSYCHOLOGY, RELIGION AND MENTAL HEALTH

1995 Bristol Templeton Lectures

Montagu G. Barker

Published by Rutherford House

First published 2000
by Rutherford House, 17 Claremont Park,
Edinburgh EH6 7PJ, Scotland

06 05 04 03 02 01 00   7 6 5 4 3 2 1

British Library Cataloguing in Publication Data

A catalogue record for this book is available from
the British Library

ISBN 0-946068-83-6

Typeset by Lynn Quigley, Edinburgh
and Printed by
T.J. International Ltd., Padstow, Cornwall

CONTENTS

PREFACE

This small volume contains the substance of the 1995 Templeton Bristol Lectures sponsored by the John Templeton Foundation and delivered in the Mott Physics Lecture Theatre of the University of Bristol. The aim was to integrate scientific studies with contemporary issues in medicine, psychiatry and religious experience.

Although some suggested an expanded text, my lengthy absences teaching abroad made this impractical. The encouragement of colleagues from various disciplines and the generous assistance of the Templeton Trust have therefore resulted in my keeping to the original format.

My aim has been to challenge the sceptic to be more reflective in analysing spiritual experience, and to challenge religious enthusiasts to be more rigorous in evaluating their own religious experience. Hopefully this will be of help to pastors, clinical psychologists, psychiatrists and to all those who try to make sense of their own spiritual journey.

My grateful thanks to Mrs Pam Lapraik for transcribing the original lectures, and to the Revd David Searle and Miss Lynn Quigley whose optimism and persistence rescued the manuscript from the desk of tardy readers, and pushed a tardy author into print. My special thanks to my wife Rosemary for her long hours of assistance in turning the spoken word into print.

JOHN
TEMPLETON
FOUNDATION

...exploring the creative interface between science and religion

This book was published with the support of a grant from the John Templeton Foundation.

— *Chapter One* —

RELIGIOUS EXPERIENCES AND
PSYCHOLOGICAL EXPLANATIONS

I have given this series of lectures the general title 'Psychology, Religion and Mental Health'. I fear that such a title could be somewhat misleading as I am not a psychologist, nor am I a theologian, but only a jobbing psychiatrist plying my trade. This point was reinforced some years ago when I was called to a country mansion on a domiciliary visit. I was told to go to the tradesmen's entrance, as only royalty and the vet were permitted through the front door. However, it was as a young lecturer in the Department of Psychiatry in the Universities of St Andrews and Dundee that I was given the task of lecturing to theological students and students in psychology on the subject of mental health and psychiatry. It is out of my involvement with those students that I come to these lectures 30 years later.

Much has changed since that time. Psychiatrists have had to reflect on the relationship between religious beliefs and the behaviour and psychological states of their patients. 'Religious insanity' was a popular diagnosis in the early 19th century. Sadly I have seen it used as late as the 1960s. The question still has to be asked: 'Is the mania or melancholia producing the religious experiences, or is the religious conflict producing the mania and melancholia? Is this merely a religious person who is manic or melancholic?' This is a discussion that still continues in clinical case conferences during which the prejudices or ignorance of the clinical team are often displayed. I recall one trainee psychiatrist stating that a particular patient was schizophrenic because in his opinion she was hallucinating and she claimed that she was hearing God's voice. When I asked what evidence he had for that, he stated that the patient had said: 'God spoke to me during my quiet time.'

There is still considerable discomfort and unease if patients describe their beliefs and what really motivates them. Most patients do not volunteer their religious views and even less their religious experiences. Most psychiatrists do not enquire about such matters beyond asking which religion and church an individual belongs to. However, it was not always so. In trying to sketch in what has happened over the past century I will focus on five individuals whose writings represent or have influenced discussion and thought on religious experience and psychological explanations.

James Cowles Prichard (1786-1848) was for many years senior physician to the Bristol Royal Infirmary and author of the first modern textbook on psychiatry. His *Treatise on Insanity* had a chapter entitled 'Religious Apprehension'. In this he stated: 'There is no subject connected with the history of insanity on which more crude and ignorant notions are expressed than on what is often termed religious madness'.[1] In his opinion most people became deranged by the misfortunes of the present life rather than the possible terrors of the next. Interestingly, he refers to the perennial difficulty in communication that exists between French and British psychiatrists. He claimed that French psychiatrists believed that suicides in England were excessive among Methodists, whom I suppose we might consider as the charismatics of their day. Prichard, on the other hand, considered that hell-fire preaching was just as prevalent among Catholics. Having surveyed the incidence and religious affiliation of the insane, his considered opinion was that the decline of religion produced a decline in the diagnosis of religious insanity but not of insanity itself. He quoted the eminent French psychiatrist Esquirol as stating that the growth of secularism in France after the Napoleonic era 'produced more instances of madness in France than all the political calamities... and [that these] were due to a loss of moral framework'. He also pointed out that statistics can be misleading. He showed that it was incontrovertible that there was a higher proportion of men and women from the Society of Friends who were lodged in lunatic asylums than those from other denominations. However, he also noted that these individuals were in asylums specially founded by the Quakers to care for Quakers as well as lunatics from other denominations. Indeed, they were there because of

---

[1]   J.C. Prichard, *A Treatise on Insanity* (Sherwood, Gilbert and Piper, London, 1835), p. 187.

the care given by the Quaker community which was effective, whereas lunatics of other persuasions were left uncared for by their own communities.[2]

The second person I wish to focus upon is <u>Dr Henry Maudsley</u> (1835-1918). He was born when Prichard was at the peak of his career. Maudsley was one of the youngest ever medical superintendents of a psychiatric hospital. He was a man of sharp mind and acerbic tongue and pen who, in his earliest publication, produced in his early twenties, referred to metaphysics, which included religious views, as a vexation. In the *Journal of Mental Science*, now the *British Journal of Psychiatry*, he spoke of science as 'affording data on which to found the investigation of the real and the spiritual, or by whatever name it is called. The enlightened mind conquers nature by obeying her... Of all values, metaphysics is the vanity of vanities and the study thereof is vexation of spirit.'[3]

There is a new note here. Whatever may have been the religious views of the psychiatrist, this dismissal of religious experience as being the product of an unscientific, unenlightened and vain mind, especially by someone who was a well-known and leading figure in psychiatry, produced repercussions in his relationships with his colleagues. Further writings from Maudsley sharpened the divisions between himself and his colleagues even more. His book *Responsibility in Mental Disease* commented that it was not always easy to

---

2   Ibid., pp. 191-201
3   H. Maudsley, 'The Correlation of Mental and Physical Forces; or man as a part of nature', *Journal of Mental Science* 6 (1860), pp. 50-78.

distinguish the prophetic from madness. He stated: 'Certainly if not mad, they [the prophets of the Old Testament] imitated very closely some of the most striking features of madness.... The character of [Mahomet's] visions was exactly of that kind which medical experience shows to be natural to epilepsy; similar visions which are believed in as realities and truths by those who have them occurring not infrequently to epileptic patients confined in asylums.'[4] A later book entitled *Natural Causes and Supernatural Seemings*, first published in 1886, summed up his views on religious writings and experiences as being 'entirely personal; they have no objective value, no voucher of validity for any other person; there is not the smallest proof that they are of any more worth than the ecstatic, hysteric, cataleptic and like raptures which they resemble'.[5]

In the same book he states: 'Steadily are the researches of pathology driving the supernatural back into its last and most obscure retreat; for they prove that in the extremest ecstasies there is neither *theolepsy*, nor *diabolepsy*, nor any other *lepsy* in the sense of possession of the individual by an external power: what there is is truly a *psycholepsy*... the outcome of an innate tendency that way: it is the individual's evil heritage from a line of ancestral development wanting in solidarity and thorough wholesomeness of character.'[6]

---

4   H. Maudsley, *Responsibility in Mental Disease* (Henry King, London, 1876, third edition), pp. 52-3.

5   H. Maudsley, *Natural Causes and Supernatural Seemings* (Thinkers' Library Edition, London, 1930), p. 149.

6   Ibid., pp. 138-9.

When talking of the saints and their religious experiences he said: 'Their follies have been the symptoms of an insane selfhood which identified itself with religion... apeing humility with religious pride and making it more odious.'[7]

Such diatribes from one of the most influential psychiatrists of his day, who held what today would be the presidency of the Royal College of Psychiatrists, even then caused concern. Subsequently there was a rift between him and some of his colleagues, a number of whom were known for their Christian beliefs, such as Dr Daniel Tuke and Dr T.S. Clouston. Maudsley ended his life a rather bitter, lonely and isolated man. He is quoted as having said that he felt that 'half [his] patients did not get well, and the other half who did get well would have been better not restored to reproductive life'.[8] It was the celebrated Dr Tuke who, as president of the same psychiatric society, wrote: 'No one will deny that the relations of mind and brain physiologically and pathologically considered, have in our own country been ably handled by Dr Maudsley. Those who most widely differ from some of his conclusions will acknowledge this ability and that his works are expressed in language which, with this author, is certainly not employed to conceal his thoughts... but we must not confound clearly ascertained facts in biology... with the theories which are

---

[7]   H. Maudsley, 'Delusions', *Journal of Medical Science* 9 (1863), pp. 1-24, quoted from T. Turner, 'Henry Maudsley – Psychiatrist, Philosopher and Entrepreneur', *Psychological Medicine* 18 (1988), pp. 551-74.

[8]   T. Turner, op. cit., p. 571.

elaborated from them. The former will remain; the latter may prove perishable hay and stubble.'[9]

Why have I chosen to comment on such a psychiatrist? It is because he was the most outstanding psychiatrist at the latter part of the nineteenth century. He was very successful and made enormous wealth. He represented a segment of professional life and the opinion of a proportion of psychiatrists at that time. When he died in 1918, he left a large sum of money to found what is now known as the Maudsley Hospital. Within 30 years the Maudsley Hospital had become one of the most influential training grounds of psychiatry in the United Kingdom. Under its director, Sir Aubrey Lewis, it became the breeding ground of professors of psychiatry. It was Sir Aubrey himself who stated of Maudsley: 'He was a sceptical scientist and a man gifted with unusual foresight whose writings would still repay perusal.' It was the popular notion that Maudsley was Sir Aubrey's 'spiritual father', to quote a biographer of Maudsley.[10]

Maudsley was a materialist and an atheist. He held his views with religious fervour. He undoubtedly influenced many in his generation and subsequently by indiscriminately grouping all religious belief, practice and experience together and in equating them with madness if they were in any way unusual, and with folly

9   D.H. Tuke, *Chapters in the History of the Insane in the British Isles* (Kegan, Paul and Trench, London, 1882), pp. 474-5.

10 T. Turner, 'After Henry', *Maudsley Hospital Gazette* (Summer 1988), p. 34.

and imbecility at all times. In that he left a legacy which has persisted in some part within English psychiatry.

By contrast, if we turn to the United States we meet a very different person who was a contemporary of Maudsley. He was a physician, physiologist, psychologist and philosopher. Dr William James (1842-1910) was famous as the author of *The Varieties of Religious Experience*, first published in 1902 and still in print. He was an altogether more attractive character than Maudsley and much more lucid in his writings. He was a visionary with a generous view of mankind. He was the brother of Henry James, the novelist, and it is said that whereas Henry wrote novels with the understanding of a psychologist, William wrote on psychology with the language of a novelist.[11] As a young man he suffered from a deep depression during which he had a mystical experience which altered his life. It was of a rather low key nature but it gave him the will to believe, and may have accompanied his spontaneous recovery from his depressive episode. After qualifying in medicine he initially taught physiology and later became professor of psychology at Harvard University. He was not a physician or psychiatrist engaged in medical practice, and it was this which protected him from viewing morbid states of mind and religious experience as wholly negative. He was therefore perhaps freer to reflect upon religious experiences with a less jaundiced mind than

---

[11]   See *Oxford Companion to the Mind* (ed. R.L. Gregory, O.U.P., Oxford, 1987), p. 395.

many clinicians before or since. He was already a distinguished psychologist when invited to deliver the Gifford lectures in Edinburgh on a subject relating to philosophy and natural religion. He chose as his subject 'The Varieties of Religious Experience' and spoke to packed and rapt audiences in 1901 to 1902.

What is not usually noted by people claiming to have read this book is that it is subtitled 'A study in human nature'.[12] His intention had been to write on 'man's religious appetites and their satisfaction through philosophy'. In the event he accumulated so much data from his researches that he confined himself to describing man's religious constitution. In his illustrations of religious experiences he tended to focus upon more unusual and 'exterior' expressions of religious temper. He admitted that this tended to appear as caricature. Basically he confined himself to recording personal accounts of such experiences. He defined the religious or divine by stating: 'It is that property which produces solemn reactions and affects the lives of people.' He concentrated on *what* a person experienced and *how* a person reacted rather than on explanations. This was irrespective of creed, lack of creed or institutional religion.

In his book he described the esoteric feelings and experiences of Old Testament prophets such as the psychodrama of Jeremiah and Ezekiel; of Moslem Sufis who would hear the voices of angels and the souls of

---

[12] W. James, *The Varieties of Religious Experience* (Longmans, London, 1902).

prophets; of Christian mystics where all senses were in
abeyance and who had feelings of being wrapped in joy;
of aesthetes and ascetics with their sense of wonder when
surrounded by beauty or having their lives pruned of all
human artefacts. James was certainly no Christian in any
orthodox sense. I suspect he would be much closer to
Don Cupitt with his stream of consciousness and sea of
faith theology than even John Robinson at his most
radical in *Honest to God*. However, his contribution was
in amassing information, presenting it persuasively and
analysing religious experiences in such a way that they
were not rubbished as madness but rather described with
coherence, thus allowing religious experiences to stand
without being explained away. As he examined the
writings of saints, worshippers, mystics and preachers
when they described their thoughts, feelings and visions
he came to certain conclusions. He believed there were
many religious systems and beliefs but that the
experience and encounter with God in nature had
common features. These experiences were intensely
subjective but had a 'feeling' of reality. He stated that
something really did happen in that their senses were
affected and they had seen visions, they touched and
had been touched and heard voices. He claimed that a
new dimension had been added to the lives of such
individuals, a dimension of *knowing*. He stated: 'It was
not a believing', as words were inadequate, but there was
'a knowledge of being taken beyond ordinary
consciousness'. Furthermore there was always a response

in that this 'knowing' had an authority which affected behaviour and resolve.

Perhaps a clinical example of this is the patient who is depressed and demonstrates this with tears, waking early, poor concentration and morbid thoughts. The feeling and experience of that depression is often of falling into an abyss, of panic and terror – the terror of total isolation and of being engulfed in a cloud which inhibits all action. What James sought to do was to elicit what religious experience felt like to that person, so that the prosaic comments of 'I prayed' or 'I felt love' took on a new dimension, where prayer came to be a feeling of being in the presence of God, and a feeling of love became an experience of being enveloped in light and at one with the world and all creation.

James saw all this as something positive which he did not seek to explain, and certainly did not wish to explain away. In a culture of biological determinism which reduced everything to changes in nervous pathways, this gained great popularity for his ideas among orthodox believers as well as with doubters and sceptics of wavering orthodox beliefs, although paradoxically his writings did confirm the suspicions which some had regarding religious experience.

The preponderance of exotic experiences within the biographic literature selected by James, and his choice of unusual saints, mystics and prophets, distanced 'ordinary' people from identifying with his data and produced a sneaking feeling that religious experiences were somewhat crackpot. Also his attempts to tie some of these experiences to personality types such as the 'once born' being healthy minded and the 'twice born' being sick or morbid minded, further fed the notion that some special personalities needed special experiences. The more abnormal the personality, then the more unusual would be the experience. This led on to the idea that religious experiences were crutches for wounded, ailing individuals. This was never James' intent, but his differentiation of personality types gave that impression.

The fourth individual whose writings were influential is <u>Sigmund Freud</u> (1856-1939). Henry Maudsley sought to reduce consciousness to neuronal pathways; William James pointed to a higher consciousness and an experience common to all men; Sigmund Freud unfolded the power of the unconscious which darkened all apparent consciousness. Maudsley dismissed religious experiences; James categorised them; Freud explained away such phenomena. He wrote three books dealing specifically with religion; someone describing them once quipped that *Totum and Taboo* killed off fathers, *The Future of an Illusion* killed off God, and *Moses and Monotheism* killed off Judaism.[13]

His earlier work was mainly concerned with observing, understanding and treating the symptoms of anxiety and related disorders arising from hidden and unacknowledged emotional conflict. His observations led to various theories, but notably that conflict was

---

13   These books were first published in German in 1913, 1927 and 1939 respectively.

derived from sexual drive. Ultimately these led to various dogmas which brooked no opposition or contradiction. His later writings were mainly turned to attacks on religion and religious experiences, and focused on seeing belief in God – and God himself – as wish fulfilment. This could be paraphrased as indicating that we are disillusioned with our fathers, and so we project a fantasy father figure in the sky for our comfort and to allay our anxiety and fear of the unknown. Dr J. N. Isbister writing in 1985 on Freud's life and work has a section entitled 'Meeting God – Freud on Religion'.[14] He states: 'Freud's religious position is crucial to his whole work.... His early experiences with his Catholic nanny, his disappointments over his father, his firm belief that it was anti-semitism that had resulted in his not receiving academic recognition, his dislike for the Catholic hierarchy, all coloured his theories. It comes as little surprise then to learn that Freud made the attack on religion one of the principal foci of his work during his last years.'[15] Isbister gives examples of Freud's comments such as 'a large part of the mythological view of the world, which extends a long way into most modern religions, is *nothing but psychology projected into the external world*. 'The myths of paradise and the fall of man, of good and evil, of immortality, and so on' were part of the psychology of the unconscious.[16]

---

[14]   J.N. Isbister, *Freud, an Introduction to his Life and Work* (Polity Press, Cambridge, 1983).

[15]   Ibid., p. 208.

[16]   Ibid., p. 210.

Religious beliefs and experiences became for Freud neurotic symptoms. Religious behaviour was an outlet for psychological forces where 'a personal God is psychologically nothing other than an exalted father.... [T]he roots of the need for a religion are in the parental complex; the almighty and just God, appear to us as grand sublimations of father and mother, or rather as revivals and restorations of the young child's ideas of them'.[17] Freud himself claimed that he was a godless Jew free from mystical propensities, as were all Jews. However, it was Sir Aubrey Lewis, himself a Jew and claiming to be non-religious, who said that Freud had a significant scotoma (blind spot) in this area. Perhaps he did have a blind spot, but the truth is that Freud was not truthful here, as Lewis and several others have pointed out. Freud was well aware of a long and mystical tradition in Judaism. His own parents came from families with a strong Hassidic heritage. He had a significant library of Jewish mystical literature, and it is the contention of one Jewish scholar that he used some of their techniques within psychoanalysis.[18] His father gave him a Hebrew/German Bible inscribed in Hebrew on his 35th birthday, although Freud maintained that he did not have a Hebrew religious education. It was Carl Gustaf Jung, all set to be his successor and the crown prince of psychoanalysis, who described an incident where Freud reacted violently to Jung's challenge by

---

[17]   Ibid., p. 212.
[18]   D. Bakan, *Sigmund Freud and the Jewish Mystical Tradition* (Schocken Press, N.Y., 1965).

describing religion as 'that black tide of mud'. Jung added in his own autobiography, 'I had exposed deep unconscious conflicts in this area'.[19] Indeed, so blind was Freud to his own attitudes here that even when the Nazis were hammering on his door in Vienna in 1938, he was resisting flight to the United Kingdom, believing the true enemy to be the Catholic church. Four of his five sisters perished in the Holocaust. Gregory Zilboorg, a Jew who became a Catholic and a psychoanalyst of high standing, spoke of Freud as 'not fully satisfied with what he had discovered and created; he seems to have had the need to undo religious faith'.[20]

All this is not to deny the genius of Freud, nor to reject his shrewd insights into the vagaries of human behaviour and motivation. But it was as a flawed genius that he resorted to explanations using 'nothing buttery' arguments[21] and constructed an elaborate system to protect his atheism and materialism. This is reinforced as he pursued his ideas with even greater dogmatism and religious fervour than many of the 'religionists'. Freud saw religion as a crutch for neurotics and religious experiences as symptoms of neuroses. Others who knew him considered that he used his system as a bulwark against an awareness of the spiritual dimension in human nature. To challenge Freud however as Jung did was to be excluded from his circle. As Dr Ernest Jones, the

---

[19]   C.G. Jung, *Memories, Dreams and Reflections* (Collins, Routledge and Kegan Paul, London, 1963), pp. 147-8.

[20]   Op. cit., Isbister, p. 208.

[21]   See D. Mackay, *The Clockwork Image* (I.V.P., Leicester, 1974).

populariser of Freudian psychoanalysis in the United Kingdom, said: psychoanalysis 'must be believed, then practised, and only then criticised'.[22]

One prominent psychoanalyst, Dr John (Jock) Sutherland (1905-1991), once claimed at a conference of psychiatrists that 'only we psychoanalysts have a doctrine of man',[23] thus suggesting that psychoanalysis provided the doctrine which gave a framework for training of future therapists. In a book which he wrote later when evaluating the work of Dr Ronald Fairbairn (1889-1965), an eminent psychotherapist and an avowed Christian, he sought to identify what he considered the emotional factors associated with Fairbairn's religious affiliations. Although Fairbairn is regarded with little honour in England, he has acquired a considerable following in the United States. Sutherland spoke of Fairbairn's ambivalence to his mother and used this to explain his identification with Christian faith, which brought him into the bosom of a loving father. When Fairbairn then transferred from the Presbyterianism of his father to Anglicanism, his mother's denomination, after his father's death, Sutherland viewed this as an indication of repression of his father.[24]

---

[22] E. Jones, *Free Associations: Memories of a Psychoanalyst* (Basic Books, N.Y., 1959), p. 14f.

[23] J.D. Sutherland, 'Training in Psychotherapy, some observations from the standpoint of analytical psychotherapy' (verbatim notes taken during delivery of lecture at Annual Conference of the Association of University Teachers of Psychiatry, London, 1989).

[24] J.D. Sutherland, *Fairbairn's Journey into the Interior* (Free Association Books, London, 1989), pp. 88-9, 132.

Returning to Freud, there is one other element that is worth mentioning. In his correspondence with the Protestant pastor Oscar Pfister, he stated: 'I wish to protect analysis from the doctors and... from the priests. I should like to hand it over to a profession which does not yet exist, a profession of *lay* curers of souls who need not be doctors and should not be priests'. Dr Isbister comments on this: 'Having, to his mind, destroyed the basis of religion, he felt he had to provide something in its place – lay (secular) soul cure'. He adds that in reply to Pfister's remonstrations Freud wrote: 'Well, for the moment I have to put up with the doctors, so why not priests too?'[25] That was in 1929, and Freud claimed he was referring to 'a very distant future'. The counselling revolution and the burgeoning of lay therapists I suspect was not quite what Freud had in mind when he wrote these words. However, the growth of humanistic counselling and therapy in the 1960s onwards would, I think, have brought a wry smile to Freud's face.

The 1960s were truly a cultural watershed in our western society. It is not my province to expand this, although I will return to the topic later. In theological circles there was the rediscovery of the Holy Spirit as the neglected Person of the Trinity. A professor of psychology in Illinois, Professor O. Hobart Mowrer, a strident critic of psychoanalysis, wrote a book in 1961 entitled *The Crisis in Psychiatry and Religion*. In his book he welcomed with excitement a small volume by an American liberal theologian named Henry P. Van Dusen

---

[25]   Op. cit., Isbister, pp. 246-7.

entitled *Spirit, Son and Father* (1958). Mowrer quotes
Van Dusen as saying that 'it is through the Holy Spirit
that all other religious phenomena and practices are
inspired and validated'. He alludes to Van Dusen's use
of phrases to describe the work of the Holy Spirit as
'omnipresence of the divine influence', 'immediately
present   and   supernormally   powerful',   'moral
consciousness', 'transcendent God in action', and links
these phrases to the experiences of the mystics, Quakers
and other writers on religious experience. He went on to
say: 'It really is a theologian taking the phenomena
described by James and linking these to the activity of
the Spirit of God in the experience of men and women,
resulting in new motivation and power.'[26]

For Mowrer, who was a non-Christian psychologist,
the uniqueness of Christ was unacceptable but the idea of
a universal spiritual phenomenon was exciting. He stated:
'What the scientist looks for in the realm of religion, if
he looks for anything, is a set of principles and concepts
which are universally and eternally operative. In Van
Dusen's book, what has previously been seen as perhaps
least promising in the Holy Trinity becomes actually the
most promising as the basis of a science/religion
reconciliation.'[27]

Such a scientist was indeed at work patiently collecting
all the data that he could. He is my fifth author, Sir
Alister Hardy (1896-1985). He was the Emeritus

---

[26]   O.H. Mowrer, *The Crisis in Psychiatry and Religion* (D. Van Nostrand,
    New Jersey, 1961), pp. 124-5.
[27]   Ibid., p. 125.

Professor of Zoology in Oxford, a biologist who refused to limit biology to a mechanistic, materialist framework. He insisted that there was a spiritual dimension in our biology which was worthy of thorough research. He was himself a Gifford lecturer in 1964 and published his lectures under the title *The Divine Flame*.[28] In his book *The Spiritual Nature of Man*, published in 1979 and revised in 1980, he produced what is in many ways an update of James who had written 80 years previously. Hardy tackled the presupposition that scientists had debunked the spiritual. He collected an enormous mass of data on the religious and spiritual experiences of ordinary men and women through advertising and pamphleteering in journals and newspapers. He then reflected on and analysed the data for common patterns and outcome using the material which he had collected over a period of 8 years, and which included three thousand accounts of religious experiences. He then described his work as a 'contribution towards the study of this important, but so little understood, part of our makeup – a contribution made in the spirit of an enquiring naturalist'.[29]

This was apparently the fulfilment of a vow which he had made at Oxford. He appears to have said to his tutor, Julian Huxley, as he was about to go to the trenches, that if he survived he would devote his life to attempting to reconcile evolutionary theory and the

---

[28] A. Hardy, *The Divine Flame* (Collins, London, 1966).
[29] A. Hardy, *The Spiritual Nature of Man* (O.U.P., Oxford, 1979), p. viii.

spiritual awareness of humanity.[30] He had a declared interest arising out of his own experiences as a boy when he was 'suddenly seized with an extraordinary sense of great joy and exaltation, as though a marvellous beam of spiritual power had shot through me'. He found this experience replicated in the majority of the accounts he studied where 'some feel a personal devotional relationship with a power... some call it God – some do not. Some see it as an aspect of their wider self... others as part of man's general consciousness.' But in so many, the feelings of trust or joy and bliss and occasionally ecstasy are dominant components of the experience.[31]

Clearly there is a question as to how far these can be called 'religious' experiences unless tied to some specific religious belief system. Hardy, like James before him, argued for a broader view of the definition of religious than something merely credal. He claimed that the term 'religious' should not be used in the sense of a particular religion but as a 'human recognition of superhuman – transcendental – controlling power and especially of a personal God or gods entitled to obedience and worship. Also such recognition should have an effect on conduct and mental attitude.[32] Hardy was convinced that the wide recurrence and broad homogeneity of these experiences, given this definition, warranted his inclusion of 'spiritual' to describe one component of the biological

---

30   D. Hay, *Religious Experience Today: Studying the Facts* (Mowbray, London, 1990), p. 18.

31   Op. cit., Hardy, 1979, pp. 1-2.

32   Ibid., p. 3.

study of man because spiritual awareness was not unusual and not deviant, but remarkably consistent and persistent. Furthermore, he reviewed the opinions of reputed scientific sceptics and found almost universally an acknowledged openness to *mystery* when pressed. He quoted Durkheim, known for a mechanistic view of religion as social function, as saying: 'Collective consciousness (in man) is the highest form of psychic life, since it is the consciousness of the consciousnesses. Being placed outside of and above individual and local contingencies, it sees things only in their permanent and essential aspects.'[33] He commented that Julian Huxley was always 'careful to point out that he was not a materialist but saw products as material when viewed from outside and subjective when viewed from inside, and that there was a great deal of mystery about the relationship between outside and inside'.[34] He then quoted Sherrington, the greatest investigator of our nervous system, as saying: 'Mental phenomena... do not seem amenable to understanding under physics and chemistry. I have therefore to think of the brain as an organ of liaison between energy and mind, but not as a converter of energy into mind or vice versa...'; and later: 'that our being should consist of *two* fundamental elements [of body and mind] offers I suppose no greater inherent improbability than that "it should rest on only one".'[35]

---

[33]   Ibid., p. 7.
[34]   Ibid., p. 9.
[35]   Ibid., pp. 8-9.

Even though Crick, the Prize-winning discoverer of genetic coding, spoke of his own discoveries as 'reducing the decisive controls of life to a matter of the precise order in which monomers [i.e. the units in a chain] are arranged in a giant molecule', Hardy questions the phrase 'the decisive controls of life'. He comments that even though the mental side of life must 'be facilitated by the genetic code governing the forms of the nerve and brain mechanism... this is not to say that we are any nearer to an understanding of the fundamental nature of the mental side'.[36] And just to be up to date, he discussed Richard Dawkins as saying that the 'evolution of subjective consciousness is the most profound mystery facing modern biology.... The idea of God... [w]hy does it have such a high survival value? From its great psychological appeal... which is none the less effective for being imaginary.'[37] However, as Hardy commented: 'Is it not possible that some of Dawkins' so-called memes [a term coined by Dawkins to explain consciousness and awareness between humans] relate to other powerful realities and that what we call God may be as real and as mysterious as is the nature of consciousness?'[38]

As I read through the vast array of experiences recorded and categorised by Hardy, I am aware of the enormous variety of such experiences. Yet it is possible to classify them. There are those experiences where the senses are affected, incorporating voice, visions, light and

---

[36]   Ibid., pp. 10-11.
[37]   Ibid., pp. 13-14.
[38]   Ibid., p. 14.

touch. There are those where cognitive processes occur along with feelings of awe, wonder, timelessness, love, security and peace. Sometimes the experiences are from within going out, and at other times from outside entering in. There are feelings of oneness. The source is sometimes good and sometimes evil. The experiences can be momentary, or they can be persistent and changing, involving joining with others in a church or organisation. Other experiences are highly private, secret and individual. Frequently there are trigger situations such as the encountering of beauty in music, depression and despair, the birth of a child, bereavement, a crisis, solitude, the taking of drugs. Hardy's analysis of these experiences is very similar to that of James when recounting certain common and recurrent features.

In trying to answer his own question 'What *is* spirituality?', Hardy speaks of an experience of *transcendental reality*. He speaks of the idea of the holy leading to the worship of the other, the mystical experience leading to a self-merging with divine reality, and claims that these are not essentially different experiences just because they are different from all other levels of human experience. He speaks of a sense of presence such as voice, love and light impinging on our senses, producing a reaction of being aware that 'it's there'.

Secondly, he speaks of *personalisation* of the experience, leading to a need to develop an I-thou relationship – in other words a communion with what many call God.

Thirdly, there is the element of what he calls *prayer*, which he claims is a common thread throughout the experiences where the person is able to communicate with this power which is transcendent but also immanent.

All this in turn affects behaviour or what he calls *experimental faith*. In other words, the life of the individual thereafter is different, having a new motivation, direction and commitment resulting in a going out in faith.[39]

His conclusion is that 'the spiritual nature of man is, I believe, being shown to be a reality. We now need a new biological philosophy which will recognise both this and the need to study consciousness as a fundamental attribute of life.'[40] That was written in 1979, and the following years have seen remarkable changes in the attitudes of psychologists and psychiatrists in this area.

David Hay (1936-) worked with Alister Hardy and eventually took over as director of his research unit. He produced an excellent book in 1990 called *Religious Experience Today – Study of the Facts.*[41] Incidentally, his work was assisted by the Templeton Foundation. Hay traces the interest in religious experience to post-Reformation Protestantism. I note this with some gratification, as it is something which I have taught for almost 30 years. In his book he makes the very telling statement that out of his 1986 survey of people who had

---

[39]   Ibid., pp. 131-42.
[40]   Ibid., p. 142.
[41]   Op. cit., Hay, 1990.

a personal experience of a religious nature, more than 40% of them said that even though they had the kind of experience described above, they had never previously told anyone as they felt it was too embarrassing and personal. Above all they were afraid of being called 'religious'.[42] It was this fear of being stereotyped that kept them silent. Hardy's research opened up the discussion to the extent that several surveys now confirm that during the 1970s to 1987 something like 35% to 48% of people had 'religious experiences'. Hay's own survey conducted in the United Kingdom in 1987 examined two thousand people from a random sample of the population and found that something like 48% had a religious experience and that 80% of these described the experience as 'an awareness of the presence of God'.[43]

I myself have met with this reluctance on the part of many people to share their religious experiences. This is particularly so as many find difficulty in discussing such experiences with a psychiatrist. I think of one depressed man who at the end of one of his sessions stated: 'You'll think I'm mad – I've become a Christian.' He was unaware that I myself was a Christian. I think of another woman who had recurrent depressive episodes who told me that one day when she was in church, quite specifically to try and get closer access to me as her therapist, she had the sudden thought: 'Why does he come to a place like this?' It was this which led her to

---

[42] Ibid., p. 58.
[43] Ibid., p. 84.

explore what Christian faith was about. Another man, who had a sudden bereavement of a close relative, spoke of his 'sense of oneness and union with God' which was associated with a hypomanic episode which nevertheless led to a new direction and Christian commitment. Yet another man, who had reached the peak of his career, spoke of a 'sudden despair... what was life all about?' On being offered the most coveted position in his particular profession he had become acutely depressed. He underwent treatment, and at the end of this episode spoke of it as being the 'most therapeutic experience of my life' as he reordered his professional and personal life as well as reaffirming his own previously neglected Christian faith.

I confess that with all of these patients I was wary and mistrustful of their experiences, and was inclined to question how far these were mere manifestations of their illness. I recall trying to keep a professional detachment from what they were telling me. Did that in itself inhibit further discussion and exploration which could have been even more helpful? If I felt that, how much more do some other psychiatrists? As a Christian, I may well feel that there is yet more to be said. Like David Hay, I am committed to a theology of grace.

Yet there is another dimension. I am impressed by the data which has been amassed. Also I am interested that so often those describing the 'experiences', whether spiritual or religious, speak of the otherness as being transcendent and immanent at the same time. Often there is associated the need to personalise the experience and pray. The experiences I have quoted also had a permanent influence in the life of the person and on their relationships with others in their families and social circle.

This surely reflects the nature of the God revealed in Christ. He is the transcendent creator of all and author of all life, whose Spirit comes alongside and indwells us. We are created in his likeness. Our being is derived from his being. Our personhood comes from this personal God with whom we can communicate person to person. This is the God who is three in one and out of whose love comes the creation of man, and that awareness of love which flows from us to others. I cannot foist my own interpretation of these experiences on other people. There are many who would strongly disavow my interpretation. But as John Polkinghorne said in his book *Reason and Reality*, 'The character of what they say is so similar to that which believers speak of as being divine, that I cannot doubt that it is the same reality.'[44]

If I turn to my own profession, I see at the present time an increasing openness to discussion of the spiritual. In 1967, by contrast, I was asked on one occasion to speak on psychiatry and religion. At that time the only published paper in 50 years of the British Journal of Psychiatry was one by an eminent foreign psychotherapist called Gregory Zilboorg which had to be published because it was an invited lecture. However, in 1991 the Prince of Wales addressed the Royal College

---

[44] J. Polkinghorne, *Reason and Reality* (S.P.C.K., London, 1991), pp. 58-9.

of Psychiatrists at their 150th anniversary meeting. He said that mental and physical health also have a spiritual base. He spoke of 'caring for people who are ill, restoring them to health... comforting them... of spiritual tasks... therapy, in the original Greek sense of healing as physical, mental and spiritual. If you lose that foundation as a profession, I believe there is a danger you will ultimately lose your way'.[45]

In 1994 the President of the Royal College of Psychiatrists in his valedictory address which was published later under the title 'Psyche – Spirit as well as Mind',[46] challenged his colleagues to take seriously the religious views of their patients. He pointed out how psychiatrists ignore spiritual issues because they think such issues are unimportant, irrelevant, confusing and not respectable. He commented also that there was an element of denial in this, as it was easier to ignore this area than explore it, as it was too personally challenging. The great taboo at the start of the twentieth century was sex; in the middle of the century it was death; what is unmentionable today is a personal experience of religious faith.

This has certainly been true in psychiatry, if not so generally. Even here however there are signs of change in that since the mid 1980s there has been an Association of Christians in Psychiatry.

---

[45]   H.R.H. Prince of Wales, '150th Annual Lecture', *British Journal of Psychiatry* 159 (1991), pp. 763-8.

[46]   A. Sims, 'Psyche – Spirit as well as Mind', *British Journal of Psychiatry* 165 (1994), pp. 441-6.

In conclusion I wish to quote from a theologian and then from a rather unlikely source, two excerpts to sum up this particular lecture. The first is by Bishop Richard Holloway of Edinburgh, who wrote:

> This is my dilemma.... I am dust and ashes, frail and wayward, a set of predetermined behavioural responses programmed by my genetic inheritance and by social context, riddled by fears, beset with needs whose origins I do not understand and whose satisfaction I cannot achieve, quintessence of dust and unto dust I shall return, who can expect much of that?

He then went on to say:

> There is something else in me; there is an awareness that truly, I am not what I am; and what I am and what I am not is what I truly am. Dust I may be, but troubled dust, dust that dreams, dust that has its strange premonitions of transfiguration, of a glory in store, a destiny prepared, an inheritance that will one day be my own.[47]

The other quotation is from Kenneth Clark, the author of *Civilisation*, derived from his renowned television series on the history of art. In the second volume of his autobiography, *The Other Half*, he writes:

> I lived in solitude, surrounded by books on the history of religion, which have always been my favourite reading. This may help to account for a curious episode that took place on

---

[47] Bishop R. Holloway (Conference Address quoted in *Church of England Newspaper*, 14 April 1978).

one of my stays in the Villino. I had a religious experience.
It took place in the Church of San Lorenzo, but did not
seem to be connected with the harmonious beauty of the
architecture. I can only say that for a few minutes my whole
being was irradiated by a kind of heavenly joy, far more
intense than anything I had known before. This state of
mind lasted for several months and, wonderful though it
was, it posed an awkward problem in terms of action. My
life was far from blameless: I would have to reform. My
family would think I was going mad, and perhaps after all,
it *was* a delusion, for I was in every way unworthy of
receiving such a flood of grace. Gradually the effect wore
off, and I made no effort to retain it. I think I was right; I
was too deeply embedded in the world to change course. But
that I had 'felt the finger of God' I am quite sure and,
although the memory of this experience has faded it still
helps me to understand the joys of the saints.[48]

The reviewer in The Times commented: 'It is hard
not to be reminded of the rich young man who went
away sorrowful... "for he had great possessions".'[49]

---

[48]   K. Clark, *The Other Half* (Hamish Hamilton, London, 1986), p. 108.
[49]   *The Times*, Review Article, 4 October 1986.

~ Chapter 2 ~

CONVERSION, CULTS AND BRAINWASHING

When planning this series of lectures I had no premonition as to how topical such a subject would become by the time this lecture was given. Firstly there was the Waco disaster in 1993, so reminiscent of the Jonestown massacre in November 1978. Then in October 1994 these scenes were re-enacted in the deaths associated with the cult 'International Organisation of Chivalric Solar Tradition' in Montreal and in the Swiss Alps.[1] In February 1995 there was the final episode of the serialised novel *Signs and Wonders* on BBC2. This depicted a family distraught, struggling with several ideologies. The action centred on the daughter Sarah, as her mother sought to rescue her from a cult in California into which she had been recruited two years previously, and portrayed her being re-kidnapped from the cult and then de-programmed.[2]

---

[1] *The Times*, 8 October 1994.

[2] *Signs and Wonders*, serialised on BBC2; last episode, 6 February 1995.

My own interest in this subject predated these events and predates also my having to deal with cult members as a psychiatrist. It dates from the late 1950s when many Christians expressed dismay that a book called *Battle for the Mind* by Dr William Sargant, on the subject of conversion, was to be published as a paperback, and therefore would be available to a wider public.[3] I was a medical student at the time, and being the kind of person I am I promptly acquired and read a copy. It was stimulating and challenging. As there had just been a major evangelistic mission in the university where I was a student, there was a relevance which made reflection compulsory. I shall come back both to Sargant's book and to that university mission later in this lecture.

The word *conversion* comes from Christian theology and is defined in Christian terms as a turning to God in which our intellect, emotions and wills are all involved. The great doctors of the church debated over the essential ingredient of that turning. Augustine preferred to see it as a total change of direction and motivation. Luther saw *repentance* as the foundation and key-note of conversion. Calvin spoke of 'being converted to God gradually and by sure degrees of repentance'. The main emphasis was therefore not on an experience, nor on a dramatic change, but on a consistent and sustained change of lifestyle and character.

It was not until the seventeenth century that the idea of conversion being associated with certain feelings

---

3   W. Sargant, *Battle for the Mind, A Physiology of Conversion and Brain Washing* (Heinemann, London, 1957).

gained importance. These feelings began to be valued as a way of distinguishing Christians who were so in name and culture only from Christians in whom the Holy Spirit was thought to be truly active. This was particularly so among the seventeenth-century Pietists in Germany. Their expectation was that there should be a period of spiritual struggle followed by a *feeling* of assurance and peace at the salvation and mercy of God through Christ's death and resurrection. It was not long before such an experience became highly prized, and was sought after and expected as *proof* of the activity of the Holy Spirit in the life of the believer.[4]

In the eighteenth and nineteenth centuries there were many periods of revival or awakening within western Christendom, particularly in the United States, when the more dramatic experiences and the physical phenomena which sometimes accompanied them were widely recorded and subsequently studied. I have in my possession an MD thesis from Trinity College, Dublin published in 1875 under the title *Convulsive Seizures: Connection with Religious Excitement*. The author was a general practitioner in Coleraine in Northern Ireland and he describes how 'in Coleraine this revival of 1858 manifested itself in its most perfect form and greatest intensity; and my residence being there I saw something of the movement'. He describes how first of all there was

> a large open air meeting, crowded with people who had assembled from all parts for miles around. This meeting

---

4   See J. Baillie, *Baptism and Conversion* (O.U.P., London, 1964).

was addressed by ministers and others in a vehement and excited style on the subject of repentance from sin, and of obtaining pardon. In the course of these addresses some of the hearers cried out in mental agony, fell down insensible, working in strong convulsions for some minutes, after which consciousness returned, and recovery took place. This occurred in numbers of instances, to the great alarm and terror of the bystanders. Those who had been 'stricken' (the term applied to those affected by convulsion) considered that they had gone through a necessary ordeal, by which they had found peace and obtained pardon; they congregated together, expressing by gestures and impressive tones their satisfaction and happiness. The convulsion was generally looked on as an essential, those unaffected by it not being considered to have obtained grace.[5]

However, in the studies of conversion experiences, whether in revival or in less dramatic large group situations, it was noticed by many that some Christians with no conscious conversion experience nevertheless claimed to be converted. Others had a very gradual growth of assurance of being converted, without any particular phenomena of a psychological nature. There were others who had a sudden dramatic experience when their lives were arrested, with a sense of great turbulence and awareness of their sinfulness, but all coming like John Wesley to an assurance of God's grace and of their hearts being strangely warmed.

---

[5]　R. McIntyre, *Convulsive Seizures: Connection with Religious Excitement* (Hodges Foster, Dublin, 1875), pp. 4-5.

It was with the growth of modern psychology that there was a curiosity as to why there was this difference among those who claimed to be converted. What actually happened? Was it possible to predict who would respond, when there would be such a response and in what manner it would occur? For ease of description I have grouped the researchers in these matters in more or less historical order.

I have called the first group of researchers, who were based mainly at Harvard University, the *Phenomenologists*. In other words, they studied the *phenomena* of conversion. They made no attempt to explain the phenomena, nor did they attempt to explain away what was observed, but they did describe what, how, when and in what way the phenomena occurred. It was a pupil of William James, to whom I referred to in my previous lecture, by the name of Starbuck, who published a book called *The Psychology of Religion* in 1899[6] in which he gave the first modern description of conversion experiences. William James later gathered much material from Starbuck in writing his own book *The Varieties of Religious Experience* published in 1902.[7]

If I can summarise their common findings, they showed in their studies firstly that conversion took place mainly in adolescence. Secondly, they confirmed the existence of a wide variety of conversion experiences from those which were sudden to those which were

---

[6]   E.D. Starbuck, *The Psychology of Religion* (W. Scott, London, 1899).

[7]   Op. cit., James, 1902.

gradual, and others where there was no conscious experience of conversion. Thirdly, they noted some differences according to whether the person was converted in a revival meeting where group and social pressures seemed to be more important compared with the person converted in private, where greater emphasis seemed to be placed upon the individual's own sense of sinfulness. Fourthly, they observed that the personality of the individual had some apparent correlation with the type of experience. William James himself described the optimistic extrovert or 'healthy-minded' individual as being less likely to have a sudden experience. By contrast, the self-deprecatory, pessimistic individual, whom we would probably see today as a person of low self-esteem, was more likely to experience a greater sense of sin and incompleteness often associated with a sudden experience of forgiveness. Fifthly, in those who had the sudden experience there would seem to be certain identifiable stages moving from perplexity and struggle to crisis and on to peace and resolution.

William James' comment was that conversion was a religious phenomenon and was 'a process gradual or sudden, by which the self hitherto divided and consciously wrong, inferior and unhappy, becomes unified and consciously right and happy and superior in consequence of its firmer hold on religious realities'.[8] In so describing conversion he had moved the discussion from viewing conversion as a purely Christian phenomenon to seeing it as a psychological phenomenon

---

[8]   Ibid., p. 189.

with no special reference to the activity of God or the Holy Spirit, nor to the truth or value of those experiences except to the individual. Also, James and others drew attention to the fact that even within a particular subculture, North American Protestantism, there was a wide variety of experiences and that personality did seem to influence the type of experience, and that sudden experiences were more likely in adolescence. There was a tendency therefore to stigmatise the person who had the sudden dramatic experience as the 'sick soul', by contrast with the 'healthy-minded individual'. To be fair to James, he also saw the weaknesses in the 'healthy-minded', whom he described as 'unrealistic' in aspects of their own personalities. It has to be noted that there were serious methodological errors in his work which nowadays would not be accepted. The sample of subjects came mainly from university students in the north-eastern states of the United States. Evangelicals and Methodists were highly represented in that population and it was not surprising therefore that so many had sudden conversion experiences.

The second stage of studies, that of the *Behavourists*, tended to focus upon conversion being merely a pattern of behaviour which was laid down by certain stereotyped procedures. In other words, they gave an explanation as to how conversions could be produced. The most popular and influential work was *Battle for the Mind* by Dr William Sargant published in 1957, which he subtitled *A Physiology of Conversion and Brainwashing*.[9] Dr Sargant was a well-known psychiatrist in St Thomas' Hospital in London. His brother was a missionary Bishop who in retirement lived in Bristol. Sargant was deeply influenced by his work with soldiers suffering from battle neurosis in World War II and how, by helping them to relive their experiences, they could return to normal life. He described how 'outbursts of fear and anger deliberately induced by suggesting imaginary terrors such as their being in a burning tank, and stimulated to a crescendo by the therapist, would frequently be followed by a sudden emotional collapse'.[10]

Sargant then likened this to an incident recorded by the Russian physiologist Pavlov, when his experimental dogs were terrified in a flood in St Petersburg. The terror of the experience extinguished the recently conditioned responses in these dogs which had been established by Pavlov. Pavlov also noticed that this experience made them more susceptible to new conditioning processes. Sargant subsequently read John Wesley's Journal regarding the religious awakening, which he found in his father's study one day. It occurred to him that Pavlov's dogs losing their conditioned reflexes, the patients with battle neurosis losing their fear, and troubled souls losing their burdens all had the same essential experience. This experience he described as

---

9   Op. cit., Sargant, 1957.

10   W. Sargant, 'The Physiology of Faith', *British Journal of Psychiatry* 115 (1969), pp. 505-18.

being subject to high emotional arousal, being reduced to exhaustion and therefore open to new beliefs thereafter. Sargant claimed that whereas William James had outlined the *psychology* of belief change, he had now supplied the *physiology*. In his work he appeared to equate every belief change, whether the change was religious, political or psychological. He seemed to consider that whether the change was produced by preaching, political brainwashing or psychotherapy, identical methods were involved in its production, and with regard to the religious experiences, it did not matter whether the religionist was in a mainstream denomination, a voodoo cult or a sect; it was still the same mechanism which was involved in producing the experience.

The response from critics was extraordinary. From the Christian world there was an acceptance of his physiology but a rejection of his equation of religious belief with political brainwashing.[11] From the scientific world on the other hand, there was scorn, notably from Koestler who wrote: 'Dr Sargant's "mechanistic approach" is the bias of a Pavlovian convert.' Koestler went on to comment that Sargant's arguments seemed to be that dogs have no subconscious mind, dog neurosis resembles human neurosis and therefore humans have no subconscious mind.[12] Professor Zangwill, then professor

---

[11]   See D.M. Lloyd-Jones, *Conversions, Psychological and Spiritual* (I.V.P., London, 1959), p. 32.

[12]   A. Koestler, 'Is God a conditioned reflex?' (Review in *The Observer*, 14 April 1957).

of experimental psychology in Cambridge, wrote an extensive three-page review in the *British Journal of Medical Psychology*. In this he stated:

> The broad – and bold – thesis of this book is that experimental neurosis, combat fatigue, abreactive arousal and collapse, and certain aspects of indoctrination and conversion, may all be comprehended within the framework of Pavlovian theory.... Conversion and brainwashing are regarded as essentially phenomena of reconditioning, facilitated by severe pre-existing physical and emotional stress.... This book raises issues of the utmost importance, not only for psychological medicine but for our whole conception of human behaviour.... Few neurophysiologists brought up in the post-Sherringtonian climate have found it possible to take Pavlov's theories – as opposed to his facts – seriously.[13]

Towards the end of the extensive review he comments:

> Ideological conversion, indeed, seems to be very much the outcome of gradual awareness of the irrationality and insufficiency of a system of beliefs and values hitherto accepted without question. Although the new system may be no more rational than the old, it is accepted because it does at that particular moment appear to the subject to square better with what he now conceives to be the true facts about the human situation. Perhaps Pavlov has indicated the beginnings of such a neurology.... But he has not – as a lay

---

[13]   O. Zangwill (Review Article in *British Journal of Medical Psychology*, 1958, pp. 60-62).

reader of Dr Sargant's book might be forgiven for imagining – already achieved its creation.[14]

Sargant paid no heed to such criticism and continued to publish along the same lines as before as in his 1968 Maudsley Lecture 'The Physiology of Faith'.[15] and in a subsequent book *The Mind Possessed: A Physiology of Possession, Mysticism and Faith Healing*.[16] His books had enormous popular appeal and it was Sargant who firmly established in the popular mind the idea that all belief changes are manipulated. Emotional pressures are the key to conversion experiences. Brainwashing and conversion are essentially the same phenomenon. Sargant himself advocated that we *should* create faith – any faith so long as it motivates someone. Some may recall that Sargant's first book was published at the time when Billy Graham was at the height of his fame and influence. Much was made by Graham's critics of the emotional atmosphere induced by massed choirs and electric organ and hypnotic singing in producing 'emotional arousal' in the Pavlovian sense. Sensitive to such comment, Billy Graham changed the style of his later meetings and I recall that when he came to Bristol in the late 1970s there was no singing and no music during the call to come forward at the end of the address. One reporter in a local newspaper commented on the 'mass emotion of the silence'.

---

[14]   Ibid., p. 62.

[15]   Op. cit., Sargant, 1969.

[16]   W. Sargant, *The Mind Possessed: A Physiology of Possession, Mysticism and Faith Healing* (Heinemann, London, 1973).

The next phase was that of the *Persuasionists*. A notable contribution was the book *Persuasion and Healing* by Jerome Frank, Professor of Psychiatry at Johns Hopkins University.[17] Frank and others believed that all behaviour was open to persuasion; in other words, that another person or persons were involved in behaviour change. Indeed, they would view persuasion in its varying guises as being one of the main influences on belief and behaviour. There would appear to be an acceptance also that all conversion experiences are to be equated, in that religious conversion, political realignment and even progress in psychotherapy have the same ingredients. All arise from a sense of need and anxiety. This can be induced, manipulated and indeed should be under some circumstances. The only variable is the belief itself.

Frank was of course a psychiatrist seeking to help patients overcome demoralisation and non-function, and his comments should be read in that light, but in his book he describes his task in the following terms:

> Three major themes develop in the pages that follow. The first is that all psychotherapies involve a particular setting and conceptual framework that specifies a relationship between healer and patient. Within this relationship, the task of the therapist – whatever his or her technique – is to clarify symptoms and problems, inspire hope, facilitate experiences of success or mastery, and stir the patient's emotions. The second theme is that the main effect of such activity is to alleviate the patients' sense of powerlessness to

---

[17]   J.D. Frank, *Persuasion and Healing, a Comparative Study of Psychotherapy* (1st edition, O.U.P., London, 1961).

change themselves or their environment, a condition that may be termed *demoralisation*. Features that combat demoralisation and facilitate helpful changes in attitude and behaviour appear in all forms of religious and secular healing in the West and in the healing methods of other cultures. The third theme is that psychotherapy may be more closely akin to rhetoric than to applied behavioural science, a position fraught with implications for how the subject should be practised, studied and taught.[18]

Two chapters are given over to the therapeutic value of religious conversion, cult membership and the religious as well as the magical roots of some psychotherapy. This is an issue which I will explore in greater detail in the third lecture, when we look at spiritual healing and alternative therapies, and the ingredients of true healing. Frank admits his own secular background and therefore quite deliberately avoids discussion of the *validity* of particular religious or cult beliefs, but he does 'show an interest in methods used to change people's attitudes and the determinants of the effectiveness of those methods'.[19] In his third edition of 1991 he speaks of the proliferation of major and minor cults in the United States numbering 'thousands', and being due to the decline in institutions and communal value systems. He continues:

Traditional religions seem to be losing their hold, and science on which so many placed great hopes appears more

---

[18] J.D. Frank and J.B. Frank, (3rd edition, Johns Hopkins University Press, Baltimore, 1991), pp. xiii-xiv.

[19] Ibid., p. 75.

and more as a false god luring mankind to destruction: not only has science failed to satisfy the needs met by religion, it cannot even tame the monsters it has created.... Under these circumstances, increasing numbers of people turn to the supernatural for reassurance. Some look inward, seeking mystical experience through meditation or mind-altering drugs: a growing number turn to astrology, numerology and other pseudo-sciences for guidance.... Others seek to gain security by attending revival meetings or through messianic religious sects.[20]

The main point of his thesis when discussing conversion is that it involves a person in need or in crisis who then goes to a willing helper with specific expectation of relief, and in commitment to this person or group leader there is healing and help and the experience of conversion. In Frank's view it does not matter whether the point of contact is psychotherapy, counselling, pastoral care, preaching or some healing context. It is still the same process which operates. Unfortunately he is somewhat careless in his source material, in that he concludes without evidence that 'conversions occur most commonly in revival meetings'; that 'a particularly powerful source of contagion is the singing of gospel hymns by the entire congregation led by a choir'; that 'emotional excitation causes susceptibility to shake and convulse'; and that 'evangelists of the past dwelt on damnation – today on the glories of salvation'.[21]

---

[20] Ibid., pp. 75-6.
[21] Ibid., p. 77.

In fact Wesley almost never preached on Hell. There is a strong impression that Frank has borrowed heavily and uncritically from Sargant without reflection or source checking. There is evidence that Sargant misread and Frank never read any of Wesley's sermons, and references to his preaching content are largely fictional.[22] However, Frank does concede that there seems to be some difference when he tries to distinguish the positive and negative effects of what he calls cults. These he defines as 'a relatively stable transcendentally orientated group surrounding a powerful central figure who influences his or her followers in a direction that deviates strongly from that of the dominant culture'.[23] He rightly draws attention to the enormous variety of movements within that definition. On the one hand there are charismatic groups within the major denominations hardly distinguishable from the general population; on the other is Charles Manson and his followers, who were responsible for the murder of Sharon Tate, wife of film director Roman Polanski, and of others in Hollywood. He points out that conversion places a person in a group which then offers enormous support for vulnerable people. This group gives meaning and purpose, and therefore motivation to overcome addictive behaviour for instance – which is greater than most therapies.[24] He goes on to comment: 'But it is almost certainly in the

---

[22] See I. Ramage, *Battle for the Free Mind* (Allen and Unwin, London, 1967).

[23] Op. cit., Frank and Frank, 1991, p. 78.

[24] Ibid., pp. 82-3.

aftergroups that consolidation occurs.' He draws attention to Wesley's experience with class meetings by stating: 'Wesley recognised the importance of a like-minded group in sustaining the assumptive world of its members. Hence he placed great stress on continuing class meetings [for converts] to consolidate and strengthen the new world view.'[25]

I would suggest that Frank was among the first to draw special attention to the influence of group processes in conversion.

However, perhaps the most interesting work has been done by the *Sociologists* from the 1980s onwards. Professor Eileen Barker of the London School of Economics is one of the most prolific writers here. Her book *The Making of a Moonie: Brainwashing and Choice*[26] is one of the fairest and most impressive studies on the topic. She was much criticised because she exploded certain myths and stereotypes. Even more helpful is her work *New Religious Movements* published in 1992.[27] This was a book mainly for concerned parents and others. It is less academic but is a distillation of research coupled with practical advice on how to view and keep in contact with a young person involved with a cult. Her work specially draws attention to the new religious movements. This seems to me a much better term, as it

---

[25]   Ibid., pp. 81-2.

[26]   E. Barker, *The Making of a Moonie: Brainwashing and Choice* (Blackwell, Oxford, 1984).

[27]   E. Barker, *New Religious Movements: A Practical Introduction* (3rd impression, H.M.S.O., London, 1992).

has none of the pejorative overtones of 'cult', and she rightly draws attention to the enormous variety of exotic groups often described as 'charismatic', 'cultic', 'heretic' and 'satanic'. The danger is that in the popular mind there is an equation of an enthusiastic fundamentalist group, which in some cultures is now almost acceptable, with a violent and destructive group like the Manson family.

Barker sought to demonstrate certain common characteristics of the new religious movements. She showed that these are not confined to the post-1950s but certainly have proliferated since then. They are characterised by their exotic provenance, often the East, leading to a new lifestyle. The movements are associated with a high level of commitment, with charismatic leadership, and appeal to the young and educated who are searching for some kind of authority, leading to their being termed 'new seekers'. They tend to be people who are socially conspicuous and many are drawn from the professions. They also tend to have international connections. Examples of the older groups include the Exclusive Brethren, the Mormons and Jehovah's Witnesses. More recent groups are the Moonies, disciples of Rajneesh, the London Church of Christ and Krishna Consciousness.

While coercive techniques are common in the recruitment or conversion programmes of these groups, 'brainwashing' is not the term that should be used. Professor Barker would claim that mind control and brainwashing indicate that the person is rendered incapable of making decisions. By contrast, 'love bombing', showering of instant affection from a group rather like some psychodrama groups, and deception, withholding the full package of a group, may influence decisions but they do not render the person incapable of decisions. She quotes one study which concluded: 'Non-physical persuasion is widely experienced in our society.... Churches, politicians, government author-ities, parents practise it in the ordinary processes of raising their children.'[28] I would add that doctors and perhaps especially psychiatrists practise it, and I will speak further on that in the next lecture.

Several papers support Professor Barker's view. Many converts are already open to views being expounded by these groups. One of the main reasons for joining a new religious movement is the need to make a gesture of independence.[29] 'Freedom to find the real me' is a watchword in such groups.[30] Finding an ideal also characterises some of these individuals, as Professor Barker quotes one member as saying: 'My parents wanted me to make religion a part of my life, but not to make it a way of life.'[31] Indeed there are some converts who have said that only in the cult could they find a place where religious issues could be taken seriously.[32] Barker claimed that there are an enormous number of *leavers* as well as *joiners*. For every thousand people

---

[28]   Ibid., p. 20.
[29]   Ibid., pp. 94-5.
[30]   Ibid., p. 84.
[31]   Ibid., p. 95.
[32]   Ibid., p. 134.

interested enough to attend a Moonie workshop, only 80 joined at the end of the week, and after two years only 40 remained associated with the Unification Church. Over time this figure diminished and it was calculated that only one person in a thousand who had visited a Moonie workshop remained in contact with the Unification Church five years later.[33]

Although the figures may vary from one study to another, the message is clear. Even when quite deliberate coercive and pressured techniques of persuasion are used, brainwashing is not common. Decision-making is retained. The majority of individuals pass through the association leaving room for the next phalanx of entrants. While many are disillusioned, many others would not write the experience off completely. Repeated comments of a positive nature are encountered, such as the group having given a sense of community, a sense of belonging and in particular time out to sort out their own values as opposed to those of their parents. Many members of the new religious movements also go on to further study and fulfil parental expectations.

The much-dramatised deprogramming exercises are illegal if force is used, and there is evidence that some deprogramming is more violent than the methods used by the cults themselves. It is questionable as to whether deprogramming is really necessary. 'Exit counselling' is a much better and more wholesome procedure. Eileen Barker makes a powerful case for pronouncing some anti-cult activity as being cultic itself. Certainly with the

---

[33]   Ibid., p. 18.

emphasis on deprogramming, a lot of money is to be made.[34]

The ideology of deprogramming says the member of the cult is not responsible, and is therefore a victim and absolved from guilt. However the person after having been deprogrammed often has a sense of having learned nothing and being little further on in life. When a person begins with a sense of loss of confidence, this may be even greater after the deprogramming and the basic problems leading to joining the cult remain unresolved. Barker instances one Briton, about six months after he had been 'successfully' deprogrammed, describing his situation in the following way:

> I know the Unification Family wasn't actually providing the answers I needed, but now I'm out, I realise just how badly all those questions are still bothering me. I feel so guilty about all the anxiety and trouble I've caused them – but I can't believe that this is what I'm really meant to be doing. I know I can't go back, but there's nowhere to go forward to.[35]

However, there are real dangers in cults and new religious movements, and those who are anxious about them and their destructive influence need to pay heed to some of the general points about all the groups into which an individual may be recruited or converted by coercive persuasion. These criteria include 'love bombing', which is a bombardment of approval. Groups

---

[34]   Ibid., p. 105.
[35]   Ibid., p. 110.

may advocate an isolation from others leading to ghetto formation which is characterised by rejection of the world and society and a general paranoia towards others. There is the creation of an 'us and them' attitude heightening the paranoia and resulting in fear and aggression toward others. There is a stifling of questions and debate leading to slavish obedience, especially to a charismatic leader. There is strong discipling by the minder, enabler, prophet or teacher resulting in high emotional dependency. There is often deception with layers of unfolding of the true cost of membership, and conflict over the sense of being deceived, while at the same time recognising reliance upon the group. There is also the creation of guilt as the member encounters the possibility of social ostracism or disapproval from the group by being 'up in front of class'. This in turn leads to a total conformism and fear of making decisions. These can be features of any group, whether religious, political or psychotherapeutic, and are to my mind coercive and destructive; they may produce a sense of peace and freedom from struggle, but they have nothing to do with the conversion of which the New Testament speaks, where a mature Christian is one who learns by experience how to discern between right and wrong (Hebrews 5: 14). In other words, by the exercise of informed judgement.

Where do we progress from here? Is there anything distinctive about Christian conversion? In terms of the phenomena of conversion experiences I suspect not. The language in which the experiences are expressed will be

coloured by previous religious teaching and the group
into which the person is converted. The behaviour will
most likely conform to the expectations and models of
that group. For example, the Charismatic or Pentecostal
group is likely to be characterised by speaking in
tongues. A reformed Anglican context will produce a
more sober type of conversion, possibly sudden but
equally possibly gradual. An Evangelical Free Church
group is more likely to witness sudden conversions; in an
Anglo-Catholic context conversions will almost certainly
be gradual. Incidentally, when it comes to personality,
outward appearances are nothing to go by. The
apparently extroverted may be a deeply insecure person.
The apparently introverted individual may be quiet, but
secure and reflective.

Secondly, I believe that the Persuasionists such as
Frank are wrong when relying on Sargant, but right when
relying on their own researches. In any belief change
there is very likely to be an ongoing relationship with a
believer. *Finding Faith Today*[36] published in 1992 was a
carefully researched survey of adults over 16 years of age
who had recently come to Christian faith. The most
influential factor in their becoming Christians was
friendship with a Christian friend or friends. What is
more, 70% of these individuals spoke of this being a
gradual process over an average length of four years.

I referred earlier to a mission to the university in the
mid 1950s when I was a medical student. There had
been an earlier mission with the speaker giving formal

---

[36]   P. Hanley, editor, *Finding Faith Today* (Bible Society, Swindon, 1992).

lectures, and after two days 35 students claimed to be converted. Within one year not one openly maintained that profession. This time the missioner came back to the university to deliver a full week of open lectures held within the debating hall. There was enormous opposition to the mission within the university, with the formation of an anti-mission committee and the missioner himself being kept awake at night by shifts of students creating as much noise as possible next door. The meetings were packed, with rowdy and constant heckling. Although something like half the university must have attended, only two students intimated to the missioner at the end of the week that they had been converted. In the next two years there were 20 others who professed conversion. All of them had been present at the meetings, having been brought by a Christian friend who had maintained the friendship over the next one or two years.[37]

As far as the sociologists are concerned, I find myself in greater accord with Professor Barker than with some of the anti-cult protagonists. As a psychiatrist I am consulted by a broad spectrum of very needy people searching for something to give significance to their lives. As I observe the dynamics of some Christian groups, it seems to me that they can be just as coercive in their persuasive techniques and as pressured in their expectations of specific experiences as the new religious movements. But the change of mind, heart and will

---

[37]   G. Fielder, *Lord of the Years* (I.V.P., Leicester, 1988), pp. 147-8.

inherent in the biblical understanding of conversion can never rest on a specific experience or on group adherence.

We do reflect and conform to psychological and sociological observations. Even Christians are human. But as Professor Barker herself says:

> According to its own rules of methodological procedure, the sociological approach is limited. It cannot pronounce on the truth or falsity of a theological or ideological position, although it can observe who accepts which beliefs and under what conditions they are more likely to adopt a particular position. It cannot decide between opposing moral claims, although it can point to the potential consequences of following one moral position rather than another.[38]

The credibility of Christian teaching comes from an examination of the life and person of Jesus Christ. Ultimately when Christians today call men and women to meet Jesus Christ, they do not call people to have an experience and to feel better. They do not call them to take up a different lifestyle and be healthier. They do not call them to bury their intellects in order to ensure an anxiety-free trip into the next life. Rather the call is to examine the life, teaching and credentials of Jesus Christ and to make up their minds as to the validity of Christian faith. Professor Sir Norman Anderson, a lawyer and Oriental scholar, wrote a book called

---

[38]   E. Barker, 'Will the Real Cult Please Stand Up, A Comparative Analysis of Social Constructions of New Religious Movements' (from *Religion and the Social Order*, JAI Press Inc., 1993), vol. 3B, pp. 193-211.

Christianity: the Witness of History[39] in which he declared
his conviction that the facts of the Christian faith were
indisputable and the Christian interpretation inescapable.
It was a Jewish professor called Pinchas Lapide who in his
book entitled *The Resurrection of Jesus, A Jewish
Perspective* agreed that as all the four writers of the
Gospels say, no less concrete an historical event [than the
Resurrection] was needed to bring the disciples of Jesus
out of their deep valley of despair.[40] Although Lapide
had difficulties in seeing Jesus as the Messiah, he
accepted the evidence of the Resurrection of Jesus as part
of God's plan.

Christian conversion is a turning to follow Christ. I am
reminded of the Apostle Paul's Letter to the Christians
at Corinth, who certainly were a motley crew when they
were first converted from their pagan background. They
often went high on experiences, and had to learn new
ways of believing and behaving. Paul in expressing the
heart of the matter wrote to them: 'And now I will show
you the most excellent way.... If I speak in the tongues of
men and of angels but have not love, I am only a
resounding gong. And if I have faith that can move
mountains but have not love, I am nothing.'[41] It was not
a *feeling of love* that he was talking about. He was talking

---

[39]   J.N.D. Anderson, *Christianity: The Witness of History. A lawyer sifts
the evidence for the life, death and resurrection of Jesus Christ* (Tyndale
Press, London, 1969).

[40]   P. Lapide, *The Resurrection of Jesus, A Jewish Perspective* (S.P.C.K.,
London, 1984).

[41]   I Corinthians, chapter 13.

about an active love, a love which persists and perseveres. Experiences may strengthen faith and hope, but following the way of love as shown by Christ is the evidence of Christian conversion.

But there is one further characteristic of Christian conversion, that mind and intelligence must be involved. In Paul's Letter to the Corinthian Church he talks about their experiences in chapter 12. The chapter just quoted is on behaving in a way which demonstrates Christian love. Chapter 14 is concerned with understanding and growing in understanding. The words 'understanding', 'edifying', 'mind', 'intelligence' and 'thinking' occur a dozen times. In many churches there are now regular courses to consider the basics of the Christian faith. The number of people who have attended, questioned, argued and expostulated in such discussions in one church in Bristol must now have exceeded two thousand. Several hundred people have been 'converted' to Christ. There is only one demand made for entry to the group: 'Please bring your mind with you.'[42]

---

[42]   P. Berg, *Evangelism Through Small Groups* (Grove Books, Nottingham, 1990).

~ Chapter 3 ~

SPIRITUAL HEALING AND ALTERNATIVE THERAPIES

There was an eminent physician in Edinburgh famed for his diagnostic skills, his brilliance as a teacher and his shrewdness in committees. He was probably at his peak in the immediate post-war era, and is reputed to have instructed his students on the characteristics of the 'successful physician' with these words: 'Ladies and gentlemen, there are three requisites for the successful physician. First there must be good looks, second a good manner and third plenty of money. Ladies and gentlemen, the first I was born with, the second I acquired and the third I married.'

Medicine has changed greatly since those days. When I was a medical student in the 1950s, tuberculosis was still a rampant killer, but by the time I qualified as a doctor it was well under control. Open heart surgery was just getting started. Antidepressants and major tranquillisers were causing great excitement, as incurable psychotics, imprisoned and immobile in their private hell of delusions for 10 or 20 years began to move, respond and take up life again. The contraceptive pill was in the earliest stages of research.

Today we can see that this progress has produced its own dilemmas. The legion of antibiotics to control infection requires constant effort by doctors to keep up-to-date. There is also a constant struggle to keep ahead of drug-resistant strains. Heart transplantation is routine in some centres, and bypass surgery has become a standard emergency procedure. But at what age do we say that the procedure is 'not available' or 'enough is enough'? Psychotropic drugs such as antidepressants are one of the largest calls on the NHS prescription costs. There is now a wide fear of habituation due to cavalier prescribing of medication such as Diazepam, which in the early 60s was confidently welcomed as being free of side effects. The control of conception by gynaecological intervention is viewed as a human right by many. But abortions are still increasing, and there are ever greater demands for special access to high technology for the infertile. The ability to perform intrauterine surgery for foetal abnormalities raises the ethical issue of transplant surgery on foetuses. It has been an extraordinary, exciting, even exhilarating five decades. Those of us born before 1940 can approach ageing with an expectation of being mobile and independent, and of being kept well far in advance of any previous generation.

On the face of it, therefore, it is equally extraordinary that the 1960s onwards has seen an unprecedented growth in the popularity of alternative medicine. I use this term at this stage because alternative medicine implies a medicine based on theories and approaches alternative to conventional, scientific or orthodox medicine. The current fashion is to use the term 'complementary medicine' or 'therapies complementary to medicine'. This is an approach which developed much more recently when the *techniques* were used as complementary to conventional medicine (often by fully qualified medical practitioners), but the *theories* on which these techniques had been founded were largely abandoned. Let me give an example of what I mean.

Dr Hahnemann's book entitled *The Homoeopathic Medical Doctrine, A New System of Physic* was first published in the United Kingdom in 1833. His translator introduced the work with the words:

> Whilst in the enjoyment of the most robust health, he commenced the use of this substance, and in a short time was attacked with all the symptoms of intermittent fever, similar in every respect to those which that medicine is known to cure. Being struck with the identity of the two diseases he immediately divined the great truth which has become the foundation of the new medical doctrine of homoeopathy. Not contented with one experiment he tried the virtues of medicines on his own person, and on that of others. In his investigations he arrived at this conclusion – that the substance employed possessed an inherent power of exciting in healthy subjects the same symptoms which it is said to cure in the sick.[1]

---

[1] S. Hahnemann, *The Homoeopathic Medical Doctrine, A New System of Physic* (Wakeman, Dublin, 1833), pp. ix, xiv.

This is followed by the somewhat immodest statement by Dr Hahnemann himself: 'It must be conceded that the true art of healing remained undiscovered *till my time.*' The italics are mine.

The second quotation I wish to give is that of a reporter at a meeting with a well-known medical practitioner of acupuncture, Dr Felix Mann. 'Nobody was more surprised than Dr Felix Mann when, as a young doctor, he stuck a needle into a friend suffering from severe abdominal pains and the patient was cured in 15 minutes. Although Dr Mann had trained as a doctor at Cambridge University and Westminster Hospital, he was intrigued enough by this piece of beginner's luck to abandon orthodox medicine and go to China to concentrate on studying acupuncture. Now acupuncture is respectable. Most of us have heard of acupuncture points and of "meridians", energy lines which apparently run through the body and which are supposedly activated by inserting needles in particular points.' The reporter than quoted Dr Mann as saying: 'Most of the stuff we heard about acupuncture is complete nonsense. In the first place, there are no acupuncture points. Nor are there such things as meridians. Over the years, scientists have tried to find these mysterious meridians, but they've never been able to.'[2] I can certainly vouch for those being Dr Mann's views, having spent an evening with him as we discussed his techniques which he felt were open to research, by contrast to the ancient theories which were not.

---

2   *India Mail,* 9 February 1993.

It is not my intention to perform a critique of alternative or complementary therapies. There are several colloquia and studies which do this, notably the BMA report on Alternative Therapies in 1986[3] and *Talking Health* published by the Royal Society of Medicine in 1988.[4] These reports were provoked in part by Prince Charles at the 150th anniversary meeting of the BMA in 1982. He claimed: 'Scientific progress had to come through logic, rational debate and critical evaluation as well as through intuitive reasoning, creative play and the ability to tolerate uncertainty.'[5] Generally the medical profession retains a cautious scepticism but accepts that homoeopathy, osteopathy, acupuncture and transcendental meditation seem to do some good, but there is no scientific evidence to support the rest.[6] Nevertheless, an increasing number of doctors are referring patients to complementary therapy practitioners. In one study it was noted that 70% of hospital doctors and 93% of general practitioners had on one occasion at least suggested referral to an alternative therapist. Twelve per cent of hospital doctors and 20% of general practitioners actually practise complementary medicine. More than 30% of the general population has tried one or more alternative therapies.[7] Another review

---

[3] *British Medical Association Report of the Board of Science and Education on Alternative Therapy* (BMA, London, 1986).

[4] J. Watt, editor, *Talking Health* (RSM, London, 1988).

[5] Ibid., Watt, p. vii.

[6] *Pulse*, 17 May 1986.

[7] *Proceedings of the Royal Society of Medicine* 87 (1994), p. 523.

on alternative therapy speaks of 'one hundred forms of therapy, none of which was fully validated'.[8]

It is quite clear that many people have felt that conventional medicine has failed them, and out of distrust, disenchantment and despair have moved to alternative therapies. Many others went out of deliberate choice. There appear to be common reasons for doing so. Alternative therapies are less likely to be poisonous with unpleasant reactions, which is precisely how homoeopathy was discovered. Alternative therapists spend eight times more time with their patients than the average general practitioner. A BMA report stated: 'Although the report also admits that alternative therapists spend eight times longer on a consultation than the average GP, it is pointed out that therapists do not hold a monopoly on the use of time, touch and compassion.'[9] Continuity is important to many people as the patient knows he or she will see the same complementary therapist on each occasion. Furthermore, alternative therapists listen and take detailed histories of a person's life, lifestyle and life events. This is especially so of the homoeopathic practitioner. Also, they struggle to communicate and explain so that the whole person is engaged in the therapy. This lay behind the Prince of Wales' comment that medicine had become microscopic and depersonalised, when he spoke at the BMA's anniversary dinner in December 1982 and said: 'Today's

---

8   'Review on Alternative Therapy', *British Journal of Hospital Medicine*, 50 (1993), p. 299.

9   Op. cit., BMA Report, 1986.

unorthodoxy is probably going to be tomorrow's convention. By concentrating on smaller and smaller fragments of the body, modern medicine perhaps loses sight of the patient as a whole being, and by reducing health to a mechanical functioning it is no longer able to deal with the phenomenon of healing.'[10] By so saying he clearly struck a chord with ordinary patients, as he similarly did on the occasion when he referred to the proposed extension to the National Gallery as a 'great carbuncle', thus incurring the wrath of some architects. A further issue is that with alternative medicines the patient feels that the decision and control of how much and how far the therapy should go rests with the recipient rather than the therapist. The element of choice is of course important and appeals to modern society. The suggestion that the patient can choose what suits best provides a 'designer medicine', where the person and the person's perceived needs are paramount.

Prince Charles only articulated what many had been feeling and practising. Brian Inglis in his book *Fringe Medicine*, published in 1964,[11] drew attention to a whole range of healing programmes which were highly popular and had a long and varied lineage. Their practitioners did not look to any rational explanation but unashamedly claimed that there was a healing agent other than and beyond the physical. Brian Inglis called this healing 'spirit healing', 'faith healing', 'power healing'. The precise source was irrelevant. He quoted a

---

10   Op. cit., *Pulse*, 17 May 1986.
11   B. Inglis, Fringe Medicine, (Faber, London, 1964).

survey which found that one million people in the United Kingdom had attended such a healer. The figure must be much higher today. He stated:

> The public has been becoming gradually disillusioned with the results of orthodox medical treatment; though reluctant to admit that the promised era when all illnesses except old age will be curable by the appropriate drug is only a mirage, and though also reluctant to pay for medical treatment if they can get it for nothing, people have begun in desperation to move over to the fringe. Fundamentally, the distinction between orthodox and fringe medicine today is that orthodox treatment relies mainly on fighting disease with the help of drugs or surgery, whereas unorthodox treatment concentrates on stimulating the patient's constitution to fight on its own behalf, on the assumption that this is safer and more effective. The therapeutic ideas and techniques of different faculties show wide variations, but they all rely mainly on the *vis medicatrix naturae* – the life force. Man has built-in recuperative powers which can be seen at work when a cut heals into a scar, without attention.[12]

The major issue here is that Inglis refused to accept the medical establishment as the only source of healing. Within 10 years of his writing this, the beginnings of an explosion of new therapies and new therapists took place. Inglis cannot have foreseen this growth, although he certainly had premonitions of it. Although often described as 'New Age therapies' they are a widely variegated group of therapies derived from the human potential movement, Eastern religions, nature therapies,

---

[12]   Ibid., pp. 236, 264-5.

self-awareness techniques, occult practices and astrology. While Brian Inglis was referred to as cranky in one obituary in 1993[13] because of his interest in alternative health, he is in the company of the great and the good. Prince Charles has sustained his interest in this area and specifically referred to the Cancer Help Centre in Clifton, Bristol in his presidential address to the Royal College of Psychiatrists in 1991.[14] An article in *The Times* headed 'Yeltsin resorts to mystic for remedy for ills' commented: 'He is reported to be receiving help from the same mystic faith healer who soothed the declining years of Leonid Brezhnev, the late Soviet leader. Djuna Davitashvili, self-styled "channeller of bio-energy" and head of a "school for alternative medicine", is a curious figure... a frequent visitor to President Yeltsin, [advising] him on policy as well as boosting his bio-energy and practising "contactless massage". The extent of her real influence is not clear.'[15] In this he keeps company with the Reagan era and its reported dependence on Mrs Reagan's astrologer. This is to say nothing of the wider use of 'personal growth and peak performance gurus' reputedly used by such as Mr Clinton in his attempts to 'salvage a presidency whose early dreams have turned so sour'.[16]

In Bristol there are several centres offering a wide range of therapies of similar nature. Some are quite

---

[13]   Obituary of B. Inglis (*Daily Telegraph*, 13 February, 1993).
[14]   Op. cit., H.R.H., Prince of Wales, 1991.
[15]   *The Times*, 13 February 1995.
[16]   *The Times*, 21 January 1995.

specific, such as the Cancer Help Centre. It offers advice and guidance about ways of improving the quality of life, but points out that the therapies on offer can be used alongside and in conjunction with conventional therapy. In its advertising material it

> offers advice and guidance about ways in which patients and their families can play an active part in their own care and recovery. In following the Bristol Programme, patients are encouraged to choose for themselves from a variety of complementary therapies which currently include: counselling, meditation, nutritional guidance, healing – the laying on of hands, relaxation exercises, visualisation/creative imaging and art therapy. It therefore offers an educational programme and not a therapeutic intervention.... It does not offer its Programme as an alternative to conventional cancer treatment. All the self-help techniques taught at the Centre can be used alongside and in conjunction with conventional therapy. The intention is to reduce side effects of unpleasant cancer treatments and enhance their effectiveness.[17]

Other Centres publish their brochures and bulletins advertising therapies available at each, with named therapists and attendant amenities of lounge, refreshments, flower arrangements and nearby day nursery. Pre-booking of courses earns substantial discounts. The therapies which are advertised as being available are for 'encouraging the body's own healing

---

[17]   *What Does Bristol Cancer Help Centre Do?* Explanatory leaflet accompanying brochure on seminars and workshops (Bristol Cancer Help Centre, Bristol, January 1991).

powers'... 'restoring natural posture to release old stress patterns'... 'relief and pleasure for cancer patients'... 'enabling anyone who feels stuck to make changes'... 'restoring energy to increase vitality'... 'finding and using natural voice in order to relax, breathe and acquire confidence of voice'.

In September 1994 *Woman and Home* published a 'pull-out and keep' insert on 'Complementary Medicine, What's in it for you?' The insert commented: 'Life nowadays moves at such a pace that it's a wonder our bodies keep up at all. This is where complementary medicine can really make a difference. Read on and find out how it should enhance *your* life.'[18] This reminds me of the African tribesman who would stop every few days on his journey. When asked why, he replied: 'To allow my shadow to catch up with me.' In some ways I suppose it is not dissimilar to the best aspects of the old Scottish Sabbath.

This emphasis outstrips the objectives of the National Health Service with its emphasis on being well, by seeming at times to become a restless, even phrenetic pursuit of wellbeing. That is a state which conventional scientific medicine based on the NHS is apparently unable to provide. The new therapies offer anything a customer could wish. What is more, there is a personalised service provided not off the Health Service conveyor belt, nor in a vast supermarket of therapies, but

---

18   'Complementary Medicine, What's in it for you?', *Woman and Home*, September 1994, pp. 67-74.

in a modern mall or gallery of bespoke therapies and healers.

How do we understand this? This growth of therapies is not without its critics. Fay Weldon's novel *Affliction*[19] prompted several serious newspaper leaders and articles about alternative and new therapies. One article spoke of the 'demand for psychotherapy which is now so great that it is outstripping the supply and is creating opportunities for the unscrupulous to step in'.[20] Another states: 'There is no law to control them – only a mass of therapeutic institutes and associations, reflecting one dogma or another, self-appointed and self-policing, awarding their own certificate licences to treat, licences to print money.... [W]hat are we breeding here? A race of benign if blinkered thought police.'[21] Another writer commented that 'the growing enthusiasm for therapy is fuelled by the breakdown of family relationships, increasing solitariness and the tougher demands of modern life'. Dr Brian Martindale, the Chairman of the European Federation for Psychoanalytic Psycho-therapy, is reported as saying: 'People look to their therapists for what is missing in their personal lives. It has become more acceptable to go to the doctor with psychological problems, but there is enormous disillusion because they have contributed almost nothing to solving the ordinary

---

[19] F. Weldon, *Affliction* (Harper Collins, London, 1993).
[20] *The Times*, 12 January 1993.
[21] *The Times*, 20 February 1993.

daily problems associated with relationships, work and families.'[22]

Is this what Carl Gustav Jung foresaw more than 60 years ago? In his book *Modern Man in Search of a Soul*, Jung said:

> Let us take, for example, that most ordinary and frequent of questions: What is the meaning of my life, or of life in general? Men today believe that they know only too well what the clergyman will say – or rather, must say – to this. They smile at the very thought of the philosopher's answer, and in general do not expect much of the physician. But from the psychotherapist who analyses the unconscious – from him one might doubtless learn something. He has perhaps dug up from the depths of his mind, among other things, a meaning for life which could be bought for a fee! It must be a relief to every serious-minded person to hear that the psychotherapist also does not know what to say. Such a confession is often the beginning of the patient's confidence in him. I have found that modern man has an ineradicable aversion for traditional opinions and inherited truths. He is a Bolshevist for whom all the spiritual standards and forms of the past have lost their validity, and who therefore wants to experiment in the world of the spirits as the Bolshevist experiments with economics.[23]

That was a remarkably prophetic statement. The only disagreement I would have is that there are many of these newer psychotherapists who have much to say. Perhaps one of the most accessible explorations of the

---

[22] *The Times*, 12 January 1993.

[23] C.G. Jung, *Modern Man in Search of a Soul* (Routledge, Kegan Paul, London, 1961), p. 267.

origins of the proliferation of modern healing approaches is the book *Let's Talk About Me*, written by Professor Anthony Clare in conjunction with Sally Thompson and published by the BBC in 1981.[24] Fundamentally in the 1960s there was an explosion and revolt against the arcane mystique and foreverness of psychotherapy as practised in traditional psychoanalysis in the West. This was summed up by Thomas Harris in his highly popular book *I'm OK – You're OK*, when he said: 'In recent years there have been many reports of a growing impatience with psychiatry, with its seeming foreverness, its high cost, its debatable results and its vague esoteric terms. To many people it is like a blind man in a dark room looking for a black cat that isn't there...'.[25] Psychiatry for Dr Harris was psychotherapy based upon Freudian psychoanalysis. This kind of criticism coincided with a period of social unrest, student revolt, riots in Paris, flower power, and 'all you need is love'. There was a new generation in rebellion, openly challenging what had been constantly questioned for the past 50 years since World War I. Now people were determined to pursue new ways of living, new ways of experiencing and new ways of healing. There was a quest for an alternative lifestyle within an alternative society, with access to alternative therapies of a physical, psychological and spiritual nature.

---

[24]   A.W. Clare with S. Thompson, *Let's Talk About Me* (BBC, London, 1981).

[25]   T.H. Harris, *I'm OK – You're OK* (Pan Books, London, 1967), p. xiii.

Professor Clare highlighted three key aspects of these therapies. The first was a new focus of American society on 'self'. He quoted an article in the *New Yorker* magazine entitled 'The Me Decade' as saying: 'What did they want to eliminate from their lives? Why, they took their fingers right off the old repress button and told the whole room: my husband, my wife, my homosexuality, my inability to communicate, my self-hatred, self-destructiveness, craven fears, puking weaknesses, primordial horrors, premature ejaculation, impotence, frigidity, subservience, laziness, alcoholism, major vices, minor vices, grim habits, twisted psyche, my tortured soul.'[26] It was indeed a 'letting it all hang out'. Clare went on to speak of the American 'hunger for perfection' plus the 'non-stop celebration of the self', which resulted in the varied and vast menu of self-enhancing therapies which included Gestalt, transactional analysis, Reichian therapy, encounter groups, primal scream, jogging, acupuncture, Tai Chi etc.[27]

But there is another aspect to which Professor Clare draws attention. He quotes a Chinese psychiatrist observing this phenomenon and writing up his reflections in the *American Journal of Psychiatry* in 1975: 'Within a society in which self-sufficiency and responsibility are highly idealised, it is often difficult to find opportunities for the satisfaction of dependency needs except in the setting of a relationship with one's therapist.'[28]

---

[26]   Op. cit., Clare, p. 13.
[27]   Op. cit., Clare, pp. 22, 26.
[28]   Op. cit., Clare, p. 24.

As I pointed out in my first lecture, psychoanalysis had a strong anti-religious bias as when Freud declared religion a neurosis. Even Jung, who tried to incorporate religion within his framework, ended up confusing the issue by using words like soul and psyche interchangeably and religion almost as a form of psychotherapy. Clare in the chapter 'A Secular Religion?' pointed out that while Freud psychiatrised values and meaning for life, Jung had nothing to offer except a mystical experience. Medicine generally shunned any discussion of the ultimate purpose of life.[29]

By contrast, the new therapists were actively pursuing self-awareness and a link with 'the other' – whatever that is. There is in many of the new therapies a pursuit of some meaning in life. One colleague once referred to this as a 'devotional humanism'. It is a complete medley with each therapy extolling its particular values from Hahnemann declaring that he had found 'the truth', to Harris in his book *I'm OK – You're OK*, stating 'here is the breakthrough'. Is there any rhyme or reason in all this? Is there any coherence?

It was Professor Jerome Frank in successive editions of his book *Persuasion and Healing* who made two fundamental observations based on 50 years of research. The first was that there are certain ingredients common to all healing situations whether organic, mental or spiritual, Christian or non-Christian, as a result of which the sufferer has a greater chance of feeling better and

---

[29]   Op. cit., Clare, p. 169.

even being cured. Frank expressed it thus: 'The most reasonable assumption is that all forms of psychotherapy that persist must do some good. Furthermore, it is likely that the lack of clear differences in the improvement rate from different forms of psychotherapy results from features common to them all.'[30] In psychotherapy he included all healing rituals and therapies whether accompanied by physical treatments or not, such as the giving of pills, manipulation, touch etc.

Secondly, he developed the idea that demoralisation is the root or generic complaint that responds to his paradigm of a person in need going to a willing helper and receiving healing. This demoralisation may be conceptualised as a discontent with self, a struggling for identity against alienation, a feeling of spiritual unrest and emptiness, or a need for something more associated with helplessness, hopelessness, confusion and incompetence. Let me first deal with the shared components of the varied healing approaches.

Professor Frank listed four features common to many different forms of interpersonal healing.[31] The first was a confiding relationship with a helping person. The 'successful patients' reported that personal interaction with a therapist was the single most important part of their treatment. The quality of this relationship was expanded by describing the helper as warm, accepting and expert. My own reflection is that this may be true, but the qualities which are most therapeutic are

---

30   Op. cit., Frank, 1991, p. 19.
31   Idem, pp. 40-50.

consistency and a persistence which creates trust. Warmth that is not sustained may imply rejection. Acceptance which does not have boundaries may breed insecurity and confusion. Expertise which is not honest about its limits can bring possible disillusionment. Incidentally, Frank pointed out how self-help books can be substitutes for helpers but have a remarkably short shelf life, a notable exception being the work of Norman Vincent Peale which has remained in print for more than 40 years. Frank goes on to say: 'The Bible is the most enduring self-help book in our culture.'[32]

The second feature common to effective healing approaches is what he called a locus or a healing setting. Most healing takes place in a special setting such as a clinic, hospital, vestry, at the altar or its equivalent at home, where ritual prayers may be said. Where there is laying on of hands or touching, that may temporarily designate a healing locale. Primarily this special space or place provides a safety where it is possible to bare body or soul. It is inappropriate to discuss or expose intimate parts of ones life or body in casual meeting, but in designated healing locales it becomes appropriate. There is therefore security in privacy and in confidentiality such as is found in the confessional or the consulting room. This may also be provided in special public situations such as a charismatic healing meeting. In that context the falling, weeping, roaring and laughing become part of the healing encounter and the permission to disclosure which does not happen elsewhere. For example, when a

---

[32]   Idem, p. 41.

man bursts into tears in my consulting room it is expected that the pent-up pain expressed in this way will not be judged as weakness. But if he bursts into tears when standing looking over the parapet of the suspension bridge at Clifton there will be quite a different reaction from passers-by. Likewise, if that person roars and laughs within the boundaries of certain well-known Christian churches, there is no consternation. Should such a person behave in the same way within the walls of Marks and Spencer, there will be quite a different reaction and possible outcome.

Thirdly, Professor Frank spoke of there being a need for some kind of rationale or plausible explanation for any symptoms or adverse experiences. By this it is meant that there has to be some point where the sufferer says: 'Ah, I see what you mean... I recognise what has happened to me... It makes sense.' Here is where the skill and persuasive power of the healer is paramount. How does the doctor persuade a person who is anti-pill but is ruminating in a suicidal way that an antidepressant is necessary? It requires persuasion to gain the commitment of someone troubled with nausea and headache and a racing heart that what is required is a chat and discussion of life events and conflicts, rather than another electrocardiogram.

Today an increasing number of people choose to go to the therapist who is able to package health and healing under their favourite brand name. There must be a common understanding. There must also be a ritual procedure that requires the active participation of the patient and the healer in the process of restoring health. This can be to increase the skill in using the technique by the patient by means of relaxation techniques, controlling thoughts and facing situations. This ritual procedure can also have the effect of enabling patients without loss of face to relinquish symptoms which they were already ready to give up for other reasons. The exact linking of procedures to the expectation of specific gains is a powerful therapeutic influence. For instance, a prescription or an instruction regarding medication is far more likely to be complied with confidently when there is a clear explanation of what is being given, how it is to be taken and exactly what effects will be experienced. Likewise there is often a great difference between the rather vague instructions of the orthopaedic surgeon about exercises following an operation or fracture when compared with the very precise instructions of the physiotherapist. Many patients can vouch for the healing qualities of the physiotherapist in making them feel and function better, as opposed to their being 'made better' by the surgeon.

The fourth aspect is the arousing of strong emotions in any effective healing situation. This is a theme which we have covered in previous lectures. We explored how emotion aroused in a situation of conflict can produce a crisis and preparedness for belief and behavioural change in some individuals. This was the same whether religious or political conversion was under scrutiny. Frank and many others researching in this field of healing, psychotherapy and altered behaviour have now amassed considerable evidence to show that pure intellectual insight has little power to change a person. But emotional arousal does seem to facilitate change of attitude by making the person search for relief and therefore more open to other influences. Many therapies employ music, art, writing, dance and drama to heighten emotion. In this way people are helped to explore new ways of expressing their difficulties and of finding release and pleasure and motivation, which in turn produce hope in overcoming demoralisation.

Perhaps a case history would help elucidate some of these points. I recall a friend who spoke of 'the most wonderful week I've experienced for a long time'. She described going on a special voice production training week, but spoke of this training as

not just a singing experience. The teacher's unique method is centred around bringing out the natural voice that is deep within us all – an earth force that starts from the soles of your feet.... We sang to the sky and across the river... emphasis was on feeling and using every part of our bodies. It was partly therapy for a lot of our group; many of them suffered a lot during the week from the struggle of allowing themselves to express their deepest feelings with this new voice they had discovered.... By the end of the week I felt I was floating some two feet above the ground. It was a magical, spiritual experience which I wish I could describe better.... We were screaming, in the natural way that a baby screams to gain attention. When we asked why we didn't have sore throats we were told: 'because you are being honest with your feelings and not thinking about your throat...'. We had to put our own feelings into each performance, and by the end of the sessions we were all in a similar state of distress as the pains and sufferings of all our fellows had been poured out over us.

When the concert at the end of the week took place, some of the family members said they had found the whole experience 'scary'. Others thought she had been brainwashed.

There is another tradition I have not touched upon, and that is the Christian tradition of healing. I recall from my schoolboy days in the 1940s a Presbyterian minister in Glasgow saying that he had discovered he had the 'healing touch'. He gave evidence for the unexpected and unexplained healing of some on whom he had laid hands, associated with a specific sensation in his hands and in the recipient's head. There were those who vouched for his humility and sincerity. My youthful scepticism was not helped by the fact that his son was in my class and was a severe asthmatic, with more time out of school than in it. Over recent years this emphasis on spiritual and divine healing, present throughout the Christian era but greatly diminished over the last century, increased and gained special prominence. It had limited acceptance in some denominations but in the 1960s came to the fore as part of the Church's ministry in all denominations, not just in denominations of a Pentecostal background. The movement received added stimulus due to the charismatic movement.

An article in the *Church of England Newspaper* entitled 'Rediscovering Your Healing Ministry' said:

> There is no doubting the fact that healing is back on the agenda of the church's ministry. At least a tenth of all the churches in this country now have some form of healing service as part of their regular care within the community.... It is important that we have a healing ministry we can live with as opposed to one we cannot. There is a variety of what I call 'house-styles' which either repel or attract, but none are necessarily more powerful than others.... I rather like the definition of Bishop Morris Maddocks, director of the Acorn Christian Healing Trust, who said that healing is Jesus Christ meeting us at the point of our need.[33]

Christian healing is therefore very much alive and well but I do not think it is pure accident that its recent rise to prominence in Christian ministry coincides with the rise in interest in alternative therapists and the new age therapies. It is to be noted how 'choice' and 'house-style' and 'what we are comfortable with' feature in the article from which I have just quoted. The plethora of books on healing in secular bookshops has its parallel in Christian bookshops and supports a thriving Christian alternative medicine. This is avidly backed by Christians keen to have personalised medicine but not always prepared to subject the claims of such Christian therapies to proper evaluation, a topic to which we will return.

But is this all that has to be said? I think not. Some of my further reflections I will keep to the next lecture, when I tackle 'Religious observance, health and society'. But there are two quite specific points which emerge

---

[33]   'Rediscovering Your Healing Ministry' (*Church of England Newspaper*, London, 10 February 1995).

from this study. First, a key issue in discussion of healing and health is the need for a relationship with a healer. It is the interaction of patient and therapist, of a person in need with a willing helper, which is the most significant element in producing healing. Hence the attraction of new religious movements, cults and alternative therapies. In other words, there is a longing to feel some kind of belonging. If our society is increasingly self-orientated and preoccupied in self-exploration, maybe the special one-to-one relationship of patient and therapist which can be bought for a fee and is terminable on both sides is the best belonging we can achieve. But is warmth and empathy the same as love? Is acceptance the same as forgiveness? If our only real belonging is to mother earth or to an impersonal life force, what grounds have we for commitment to each other in suffering pain, in working through difficulties and in forgiving and being forgiven in order to restore relationships? We can only really know ourselves as we are truly known in committed belonging. That means giving up something of ourselves. Yet this is the relationship which brings belonging.

The other issue is that of hope and change. Thomas Harris in his book *I'm OK – You're OK* says:

> This book is the product of a search to find answers for people who are looking for hard facts in answer to their questions about how the mind operates, why we do what we do, and how we can stop doing what we do if we wish. The answer lies in what I feel is one of the most promising breakthroughs in psychiatry in many years. It is called Transactional Analysis. It has given hope to people who have

become discouraged by the vagueness of many of the traditional types of psychotherapy. It has given a new answer to people who want to change rather than to adjust, to people who want transformation rather than conformation.[34]

Here is an echo of Jerome Frank. But it is also close to the language of religion as we have seen in this series and demonstrates how psychologists and psychiatrists cannot leave religion alone. They are always coming back to it. This is because as human beings we seem to need religion and as psychiatrists and psychologists we are in the business of fulfilling needs. It is especially true of the new counsellors and alternative therapists who are clearly flourishing. 'Spirituality' is a watchword. There are a thousand and one different varieties. Is it just getting in touch with deeper consciousness? Is it a life force we tap into? Or is the Lord, the Creator of Life, the person to whom ultimately we belong? Carl Gustav Jung stated:

> Among all my patients in the second half of life – that is to say, over thirty-five – there has not been one whose problem in the last resort was not that of finding a religious outlook on life. It is safe to say that every one of them fell ill because he had lost that which the living religions of every age have given to their followers, and none of them has been really healed who did not regain his religious outlook. [35]

This we will look at in the final lecture.

---

34 Op. cit., Harris, p. xiii.
35 Op. cit., Jung, 1961, p. 264.

~ Chapter 4 ~

RELIGIOUS OBSERVANCE, HEALTH AND SOCIETY

or 'Is Religion Good for You?'

In the previous lecture I quoted from Carl Gustav Jung, who wrote his book *Modern Man in Search of a Soul* in 1933. In it he summed up his position on religion and healing, concluding with the view that none of his patients had been healed without regaining their religious outlook. Many years have passed since then. Concepts of health and healing have changed. Attitudes to religion have changed. But recently this refrain has become stronger. A reviewer of some recent work assessing the impact of religious observance on the health of individuals states that research has clearly shown that 'What is good in the moral sense in the city of God is also good in the pragmatic sense in man's country.'[1] I propose to look more fully at some of the studies and research which examine this.

---

[1]   P. Yancey, 'Health and the God Factor', *Christianity Today* 36, no. 14 (1991), p. 88.

RELIGION AND PHYSICAL HEALTH

A psychiatrist by the name of David Larson and his colleagues in the United States wrote a key paper entitled 'Associations between Dimensions of Religious Commitment and Mental Health'. In this paper they gave a review of all the publications on this theme in the *American Journal of Psychiatry* and *Archives of General Psychiatry* between the years 1978 and 1989. They were looking for papers which mentioned any aspect of religious belief or practice and health. Larson was particularly interested in mental health but discovered incidentally that a number of papers also commented on physical health.

In a general summary he stated that regular worshippers live longer. Religiousness markedly reduces the incidence of heart attack and associated conditions such as arteriosclerosis, raised blood pressure and strokes. Even the religious man who smokes is seven times less likely to have blood pressure problems than the non-religious smoker. Religious people were less likely to abuse alcohol and far less likely to use illicit drugs. By contrast, 40% of alcoholics had abandoned religious faith in their teens. Religious commitment also offers some protection against one of the greatest social producers of health problems – divorce. People who attend church regularly are more than twice as likely to remain married. One study commented that 'not going to a religious service or rarely going should be regarded as a definite health risk factor'.[2] Perhaps we should consider this as we decide how to spend part of Sunday.

To take this a little further, divorce is now recognised in the United States to be associated with an increase of early death from strokes, raised blood pressure, lung cancer and bowel cancer. The British statistics are equally convincing regarding the physical sequelae of divorce, especially among men. Likewise, the impact of divorce on children has now been researched over several decades in national surveys in both the United States and the United Kingdom. *The Exeter Family Survey*, an intensive study of a cohort of families in the West Country, shows that physical ill health in children is one of the most striking results of family break-up. The study compared intact families where there was minimal parental conflict with families with considerable conflict, families where there had been divorce, and what are called 'reordered families' where one or other of the parents has acquired a new partner. There was evidence for accidents being more severe, disabilities more difficult to overcome, hospitalisation longer and psychosomatic illness greater in families in the last three categories.[3]

These studies suggest that people from a Judaeo-Christian background who are sufficiently committed to their religion to attend worship and to participate with

---

[2] D.B. Larson et al., 'Associations between Dimensions of Religious Commitment and Mental Health', *American Journal of Psychiatry* 149 (1992), pp. 557-9.

[3] M. Crocker and J. Tripp, *The Exeter Family Study* (University of Exeter Press, Exeter, 1994).

fellow believers, also watch their lifestyle in particular ways. These include drinking alcohol in moderation or being totally abstinent, smoking little or not at all, avoiding other drugs, and remaining faithful within the marital relationship. It may be that these by-products of a Judaeo-Christian view of life are effective in protecting health. But the key factor is religious commitment rather than a particular affiliation. Dedicated Mormons, Jews, Catholics and Protestants all have improved health. There is evidence also that the *strength* of the belief promotes health.

Papers on the elderly in hospital with physical illness have demonstrated that people with strong religious views and commitment are much less likely to develop depression post-operatively, and also have fewer complications. One survey of elderly women recovering from hip fractures showed that those who were least depressed and could walk furthest at discharge were those to whom God was a source of strength and comfort and who attended religious services.[4] Accordingly, religious belief and commitment would appear to increase their recovery potential. Perhaps an index of religiousness should be part of a predictor regarding the recovery process.

4   P. Pressman et al., 'Religious Belief, Depression and Ambulation Status in Elderly Women with Broken Hips', *American Journal of Psychiatry* 147 (1990), pp. 758-60.

RELIGION AND MENTAL HEALTH

If we turn specifically to the realm of mental health, there has been an enormous amount of literature in recent years. When I reviewed this topic in 1967 at a post-graduate conference there had been only one paper in the previous 50 years in the *Journal of Mental Science* and its successor the *British Journal of Psychiatry* specifically on the subject of religion. Recently there have been four significant contributions in three years, and others of lesser importance, though specific empirical research in this area is still largely confined to the United States.

Larson in the review already mentioned commented that 72% of the measures of religious commitment used in the surveys were shown also to benefit mental health. Four of these measures brought significant benefit in 92% of the instances. These were participation in religious services, social support, prayer and perceived relationship with God. The other measures of religious commitment which were rather less specific and included such terms as 'religious meaning' with no explanation given were associated with negative influences or were not significant in terms of mental health.[5]

A further review of references to religion in the *Journal of Family Practice* over a period of 10 years[6]

---

[5]   Op. cit., Larson et al., 1992.

[6]   F.C. Craigie, D.B. Larson and I.Y. Liu, 'References to Religion in the *Journal of Family Practice*. Dimensions and Valence of Spirituality', *Journal of Family Practice* 30 (1990), pp. 477-8.

showed that the same factors that Larson identified were beneficial to health in 83% of the papers and produced a neutral evaluation in only 17%. To some extent these results depend on the definition of 'mental health'. Some papers were more concerned with the absence of mental illness; others were concerned with the absence of symptoms and attitudes leading to life impairment. Most of the papers were less concerned with the 'feel good' factor.

In a multi-author review of most of the literature on religion and mental health published by Oxford University Press in 1992[7] most of the authors had no religious stance. The papers covered the effects of religious attitudes and belonging on such varied topics as suicide, women's health, depression, fear of death, guilt, self-esteem, rationality, self-actualisation, meaning in life, psychological well-being, mental health in early life, mental health in later life, marital adjustment, crime and delinquency, and substance abuse. There were other papers on membership of cults and even the effects of irreligion on mental health. In an excellent foreword the editor summarises the evidence as showing that religion does seem to be beneficial to mental health. Religious belief is associated with a reduction of existential anxiety, and gives a sense of hope and meaning. It enables a person to withstand suffering and pain as it offers ways of understanding some of life's conflicts. Religious belief also gives a sense of power through an

---

[7]   J.F. Schumaker, editor, *Religion and Mental Health* (O.U.P., Oxford, 1992).

outside omnipotent force, gives moral guidelines and a sense of belonging with other like-minded people. The editor somewhat wryly and perhaps slightly cynically quotes the comment that psychologically 'religion is equivalent to an elaborate rescue operation in life'.[8] In less emotive terms the research could be summed up as showing that religious belief is associated with an awareness of ones own needs, of having a direction in life influencing choices and behaviour, and of having the ability to relate to other people in a mutually supportive way.

The editor then sought to summarise the negative and detrimental aspects of religious belief toward mental health. He noted the occurrence of unhealthy levels of guilt, low self-esteem, self-denigration, unhealthy repression of anger, fear of punishment, dependency and sexual maladjustment. The division of the world into saints and sinners could produce a paranoid thought pattern and a suspension of rational and critical thought. My own reflection on this series of negative findings is that most of the studies were of people from a Judaeo-Christian background. There *is* a 'worm theology' within some Christian teaching which is damaging to certain personalities and is rightly highlighted in these papers. But I would dispute the view that equates mental health with self-sufficiency, letting it all hang out, and with the freedom to experiment sexually, homosexually, heterosexually, pre- and post-maritally; and suggests that

---

8   Ibid., p. 3.

to have problems in these areas indicates poor mental health.

Some of the papers were extreme in their basic assumption that to be religious indicates mental sickness and that by definition religion is dehumanising. Others began from the position that to be religious is to be in contact with ultimate reality and therefore religiously biased psychotherapy is innately superior to other forms. Most papers took a more reasoned middle ground, that religion had the potential to be either positive or negative in its effects on mental health. One of the contributors to the volume summarised research in this area by saying: 'With regard to mental health, empirical research shows that religion can be a haven, a hazard, a therapy, an expression or a suppressing of mental pathology. The old question of whether religion is right or wrong and whether it is the cause or remedy for mental disease has proved fruitless.'[9]

I think there are quite clear results which emerge from these reviews of the literature in English over the past 20 years. A high degree of religious commitment in terms of frequent attendance at worship services, with active participation in church or synagogue activities, is associated with observable and measurable positive effects upon aspects of physical and social behaviour. These in turn have some positive impact on people who are vulnerable to mental illness and emotional difficulties. Also the more objective the indications of

---

[9]   Ibid., p. 40.

mental health and illness such as blood pressure ratings, suicide, violence, alcoholism and drug abuse, divorce, and speed of physical rehabilitation, then the clearer is the correlation with measures of religiousness. Participation in religious services, support, prayer and a perceived relationship with God – which could be summarised as 'believing and belonging' – is a combination which seems to be associated with the positive benefits of being religious. Accordingly the harder the data for measuring religiousness and the harder the data for assessing mental health, the greater the correlation between religiousness and mental health.[10]

There is a fourth theme in these papers. This is that *small* amounts of religion can actually be detrimental to mental health. In other words, the less active the commitment and belief in terms of involvement with fellow believers, the higher the levels of worry, anxiety and guilt. This is in accord with the work of Gordon Allport, a psychologist writing in the 1960s.[11] He stated that there were two types of religious commitment. There was what he called *extrinsic* religion which he equated with social conformity. In other words, religion was a means to an end. The person's goals were to be

---

[10]   J. Gartner, D.B. Larson and G.D. Allen, 'Religious Commitment and Mental Health: A Review of the Empirical Literature', *Journal of Psychology and Theology* 19 (1991), pp. 6-15.

[11]   G.W. Allport and J.M. Ross, 'Personal Religious Orientation and Prejudice', *Journal of Personality and Social Psychology* 5 (1967), pp. 432-43.

accepted, to reap social benefits and to do the accepted thing. These people's religiousness had a negative correlation with mental health. By contrast, *intrinsic* religion was to be equated with deep personal commitment. In these people religion mattered intensely. It was an end in itself and summed up what life was about. There was a positive correlation between this kind of religion and measures of mental health.

There is other supportive evidence of this of a rather teasing nature. There are now three decades of research on attitudes to dying. Those most at peace at the point of dying are the religiously committed with a strong belief in the afterlife, as well as the totally non-religious with a strong belief in no afterlife.[12] Presumably this is because both know where they are going. It reminds me of the story of the Reverend H. Burden, a noted West Country philanthropist and provider of services for the mentally handicapped in the early part of the nineteenth century. He had a coachman who was an atheist, and who was reported as having said to his employer on one occasion; 'I can't make up my mind whether you're a saint destined for heaven or a rascal doomed to hell.' Burden replied: 'You'll never know, will you?'

There has been less research into the effects of *irreligion* – and committedness to irreligion – on mental health. Christian believers have often noted the fate of Nietzsche, who ended his life insane and paranoid having written the book *The Antichrist*[13] shortly before. In this

12   J. Hinton, *Dying* (Penguin, Harmondsworth, 1972).
13   F. Nietzsche, (Penguin, Harmondsworth, 1968). First published 1895.

book he spoke of his rejection, abjuration and abhorrence of the pallid Galilean. I recall reading an autobiographical account by the late A. J. P. Taylor, the Oxford historian. He spoke of his 'conversion experience' which he recalled with clarity decades later. He recounted how he was standing looking out of the headmaster's window at school and had an experience which filled him with joy, lifted a load from his shoulders and was associated with the sudden conviction that 'there is no God'. He claimed it was an experience for which he was grateful for the rest of his life and which he saw no reason to question or reconsider.[14]

In his book *Mental Illness and Social Structure*, the sociologist Bernard Ineichen wrote:

> If church membership and attendance continue to fall, the question that should be asked is: 'Can societies operate with a satisfactory level of mental health, but without any widespread religious practices or even belief in God?' The mental health of agnostic or atheistic societies is an even more open question than those we have been attempting to answer. The world has never seen one before, and as yet history provides no guidelines.[15]

That was written in 1979, when the opportunities for such research were not possible. Perhaps some psychiatrists and researchers in the field of physical and mental health would care to explore these issues within

---

[14] A.J.P. Taylor, *A Personal History* (Hamish Hamilton, London, 1983).
[15] B. Ineichen, *Mental Illness and Social Structure* (Longmans, London, 1979), p. 53.

some of the societies which are now more open to research of that nature compared with a decade or more ago.

There is the further issue of how we define mental health. One study pointed out that the beneficial results of religion depended on one's definition. If mental health is to be equated with acceptable behaviour and with freedom from guilt and worry, then there is no special correlation with religiousness. If, on the other hand, mental health is to be equated with a feeling of being in control of one's life, with positive feelings about oneself and of being flexible, open-minded and flowing with the tide, then there is a negative correlation with religion.[16] This could be for the obvious reason that the orthodox Christian, Jew and Muslim believes that God is ultimately in control and he alone is Lord. For Christians at least we are guilty sinners before his holiness, who are recipients of grace and forgiveness and engaged to fight valiantly against sin, flesh and the devil. However, if mental health is to be equated with the absence of mental symptoms and illness, then there is a strong positive correlation with religiousness – and that is the bias of the studies we have surveyed in this lecture.

OTHER RELIGIONS

There are very few *empirical* studies on the effect of religions other than Christianity and Judaism on mental

---

[16] C.D. Batson and W.L. Ventis, *The Religious Experience* (O.U.P., New York, 1982).

health and little comparable material from groups where other religions provide the prevailing culture. There are several studies on Buddhism and its practices of meditation and asking paradoxical questions which note the similarities between Buddhist practices and certain current behavioural therapies. There are increasing studies on aryuvedic texts and mental health. It is of interest that Dr Sudhir Kakar, an Indian psychoanalyst based in Delhi, writing from an Indian context states that in spite of different concepts of mental health in West and East, there are an increasing number of Indians who are seeking out western-style psychotherapy with its Judaeo/Christian roots. He observes that they no longer depend upon the more traditional healing strategies which are deeply rooted in Hindu life and tradition.[17]

The question may remain therefore in some minds: 'Is one religion better for you than another?' The older psychologists clearly did not wish to be drawn into that discussion. In fact they openly declared their belief that it was an improper question. William James stated:

> It would never do for us to place ourselves offhand at the position of a particular theology, the Christian theology, for example, and proceed immediately to define the 'more' as Jehovah, and the 'union' as his imputation to us of the righteousness of Christ. That would be unfair to other religions, and from our present standpoint at least, would be an over-belief.[18]

---

[17]   S. Kakar, *Shamans, Mystics and Doctors* (Unwin, London, 1982), p. 275.
[18]   Op. cit., James, 1902, p. 511.

Carl Gustav Jung at the end of the declaration with which I began this lecture, goes on to say: 'This [religious outlook] of course has nothing whatever to do with a particular creed or membership of a church.'[19]

Robin Skynner and John Cleese in their book *Life and How to Survive It* have an extensive section on religion, spiritual experience and values and the link between mental health and religious experience. John Cleese comments in the dialogue within the book: 'You're making that link a lot tighter than I'm comfortable with.' Skynner made clear his own personal leanings towards Buddhism because of its perceived absence of theologies and espousal of meditation. He stated: 'A preoccupation with theological beliefs is usually a substitute for spiritual experience and can even stand in the way of it.'[20]

I perceive a shift of opinion in the modern preparedness to express preferences which are personal rather than empirically researched. There is no empirical, psychological or any other form of research which can demonstrate the truth of a particular religion or irreligion. But it seems to me that certain things can be said to be true from the research and data which we have studied in these lectures. There is a deep hunger for specific religious or – more broadly – spiritual experience which is associated with some kind of believing. But while believing gives a foundation and a focus to life,

---

19   Op. cit., Jung, 1933, p. 264.
20   R. Skynner and J. Cleese, *Life and How to Survive It* (Methuen, London, 1993), pp. 307, 303.

active and participatory belonging – such as friendship, fellowship, and membership of the family of fellow believers – is associated with better health, physical and mental, according to the measures I have indicated.

At the same time it is possible for the presentation of the theological truths undergirding that belonging to be destructive of mental health especially for some people. Dr James Packer, in his popular and much translated book *Knowing God* states:

> There is a certain type of ministry of the gospel which is cruel.... There is a glamorisation of Christian joy which buys results with false hopes.... There is another type of ministry which sentences Christians to a treadmill life of hunting each day for non-existing failures in consecration, in the belief that if only they could find some failures to confess and forsake they could uncover an experience of spiritual infancy which God means them now to leave behind.[21]

We discussed earlier how there can be a stifling, personality-binding and inhibitory quality to some Christian groups, not just cults, which can damage and maim some souls. Many autobiographies bear eloquent testimony to this, a classic being *Father and Son* by Edmund Gosse.[22] I spend a considerable amount of my time dealing with these issues with patients referred to me by their family doctor. I have commented elsewhere that many religious patients refuse to examine how little

---

[21] J.I. Packer, *Knowing God* (Hodder, London, 1973), pp. 221-2.

[22] E. Gosse, *Father and Son* (Penguin, Harmondsworth, 1989).

thought-through and reality-based their own faith has been.[23] To quote James Packer again: 'Unreality in religion is an accursed thing. We need God to make us realists about both ourselves and him.'[24]

In conclusion, Dr Jock Sutherland to whom I have already referred, when speaking at a conference of university teachers of Psychiatry on the subject 'Assumptions and Preconceptions about Psychotherapy', quoted Sir Peter Medawar as saying that 'the scientific paper is a fraud'. In other words, even when we are trying to be completely objective we have our own assumptions, preconceptions and even prejudices. Professor Cawley on the same occasion agreed, saying that when going through Customs it seems only fair to declare one's contraband.[25] May I be open and display my baggage and declare my own position?

Ever since starting the practice of psychiatry and having to deal with the sufferings, anguish, hell, rejections, abuse and fears which form the story of so many of my patients, I have struggled as to how to bring what I believe to be the gospel into my therapy. There are those who set up specifically Christian hospitals, Christian therapeutic programmes and counselling based on a Christian world-view. Christian Counselling Centres are now widespread in the United Kingdom. In

---

23   M.G. Barker, 'Man – Dust with a Destiny', in *Real Science, Real Faith*, R.J. Berry, editor (Monarch, Eastbourne, 1991), p. 170.
24   Op. cit., Packer, 1973, p. 228.
25   Op. cit., Sutherland, 1989. (Unpublished proceedings of the Association of Teachers of Psychiatry Conference, London, 1989).

the United States, evangelical Christians have contracted to take on the running of psychiatric wings of general hospitals. Their aim is to provide specific Christian treatment with Christian staff. The providers apparently are delighted as this enables them to fill empty beds. The purchasers are delighted with the service. The funders are the private medical insurance schemes.

Apart from my reservations about this approach, I am in a different position. I work in a secular context. As I enter into the suffering of my patients, I must be deeply involved and yet must see a possibility of help and some hope for a way forward. The patient must be able to talk to someone who can enter into the problem without being overwhelmed. Surely this is the Christian understanding of Christ's incarnation, crucifixion and resurrection? The Jewish Rabbi, Chaim Potok, in his novel *My Name is Asher Lev*[26] wrote of a Jewish artist who found that the only way he could portray the alienation within his family was by painting a crucifixion scene entitled 'The Brooklyn Crucifixion'. When it comes to dealing with broken and disturbed relationships I can listen to the anguish, hurt and bitterness; I can accept the rejected person suffering from a wrong done to them as well as accepting the rejecting individual who feels justified in the wrong done to another. But there has to be love and the loss of bitterness for any healing to take place. For true love to flow there has first to be an acknowledgement that wrong has been done.

---

[26]   C. Potok, *My Name is Asher Lev* (Penguin, Harmondsworth, 1974).

The highly popular author, Scott Peck, entitled his first book *A Road Less Travelled: a New Psychology of Love.*[27] He then felt the need to write a second book 10 years later called *People of the Lie: the Hope for Healing Human Evil.*[28] Even so, it seems to me that forgiveness is still evaded, and yet this is what is essential to the true healing of relationships. Psychotherapy accepts the past for what it is. It does this without glossing over or indeed exaggerating, but seeks to put the past where it belongs so that the person is no longer in bondage to it. Forgiveness however looks at the wrong, sees it as the wrong and evil that it is and then because it is wrong goes on to say 'I will not tolerate this, I will not allow it to destroy the relationship.' As one theologian put it: 'There is an active change in attitude which seeks to build the relationship creatively from the shared facing of what has been wrong.'[29] Forgiveness is thus part of the love which casts out fear; the love which extends itself for the sake of the other's growth. It has to do with breaking down idealisation and recognising in oneself and others both good and bad, and learning to live with that. It comes from an awareness that God loves us in spite of our wrong-doings. By alleviating guilt, forgiveness can be a most powerful contribution to mental health.

---

[27] M. Scott Peck, *A Road Less Travelled: A New Psychology of Love* (Simon and Schuster, New York, 1978).

[28] M. Scott Peck, *People of the Lie: the Hope for Healing Human Evil* (Simon and Schuster, New York, 1983).

[29] D. Atkinson, 'From the Stove to the Skin Horse: Theology, Religion and Mental Disorder', *Anvil* 6 (1989), pp. 199-207.

Accordingly as I seek to help people through the impasse of broken relationships I try to point out two alternative ways of proceeding. We can view relationships as being a 50/50 contract where we keep up our commitment so long as the other person keeps up their part of the bargain. If I am short-changed then I can reduce my commitment to 40% in exchange for 40%, and eventually zero for zero. Or we can offer a 100% relationship both ways. In this situation even if short-changed we keep up our commitment, recognising the wrong, not denying or minimising its pain, but keeping up our commitment and working out ways of how to restore the situation. That needs time, commitment and a basis for doing so. It was Rollo May, an American psychotherapist, who observed of many couples that they never stayed long enough together to discover what it was to love.[30]

By contrast, his contemporary Fritz Perls, the founder of Gestalt therapy, was the seeker of the liberating experience, the father of self-discovery and inventor of the phrase 'doing your own thing'. His Gestalt prayer is in sharp contrast:

> 'I do my thing and you do your thing.
> I am not in this world to live up to your expectations.
> You are not in this world to come up to mine.
> You are you and I am I.
> And if by chance we find each other it's beautiful.
> If not, it can't be helped.'[31]

---

[30] R. May, *Love and Will* (Collins, London, 1972).

[31] M. Shepard, *Fritz* (Bantam Books, New York, 1976), p. 3.

We can go after spiritual experiences, new beliefs and new belongings; we can follow the gurus of the 'feel good' factor. As Woody Allen succinctly put it: 'More than any time in history mankind faces a cross-road. One path leads to despair and utter hopelessness, the other to total extinction. Let us pray that we have the wisdom to choose correctly.'[32]

Or we can listen to a man, known as Saul of Tarsus before his conversion experience, and Paul after it, when he wrote: 'The love of Christ leaves us no choice when once we have reached the conclusion that one man died for all.'[33] This changes radically the way in which we view all human relationships. As Christians our aim is to share the love of Christ and experience now the effects of the healing and reconciling work which he completed through his death. The New Testament enlightens the text-book of Psychiatry; the Holy Spirit of God is present at every encounter. The Biblical themes of forgiveness, faithfulness, justice, trust in the midst of despair and many more inform our practice and give us hope in the face of the bleakest and most discouraging situation which may confront us in the consulting room. The parameters of our existence are contained in the words of the communion service: 'Christ has died; Christ is risen; Christ will come again.'

---

[32]   Quoted from S. Dunant and R. Porter, editors, *The Age of Anxiety* (Virago, London), p. xviii.

[33]   New English Bible, 2 Corinthians 5 :14